Elizabeth had been wildly in love with Damian Hayes, but his jealousy had been too much for her and two years ago they had parted. And now she had heard that he was dead. To try and exorcise the grief, she went back to France where they had once been so happy—but found instead that she was haunted by the memory of him as never before . . .

HAUNTED

BY

CHARLOTTE LAMB

MILLS & BOON LIMITED
15–16 BROOK'S MEWS
LONDON W1A 1DR

First published 1983
Australian copyright 1983
Philippine copyright 1983
This edition 1983

© Charlotte Lamb 1983

ISBN 0 263 74360 8

Set in Monophoto Plantin 11 on 12 pt.
01–1083 – 47505

Made and printed in Great Britain by Richard Clay (The Chaucer Press) Ltd, Bungay, Suffolk

CHAPTER ONE

ELIZABETH hadn't even caught the man's name,
she had barely looked at him since they were
introduced. He had been doing all the talking, he
was a small, spare man in his fifties with a strong
Bronx accent and very expensive clothes, she kept
seeing a wide gold ring flashing on his hand as he
gestured. It was a business party, but he wasn't
one of their clients, so Elizabeth could be polite
without worrying over much about listening to
him, and her mind kept wandering. She was idly
looking at the paintings hanging on the walls of
the penthouse, when one of them made her
breath catch. She hadn't noticed it before, it was
half hidden by a huge pot of green ferns which
seemed almost to grow out of the picture as she
stared. She remembered it so well. She had sat on
damp grass on that riverbank, watching Damian
paint it: a water picture, cool and tranquil, all
silver and green, with willows, and wild geese
flying overhead, their grey-brown breasts
repeated in the stormy sky behind them.

'Beautiful technique he had,' the man standing
beside her said, and she looked at him, open-
eyed.

'Sorry?'

'Damian Hayes,' he said. 'That's what you were
looking at, wasn't it? He did it a couple of years
ago, his style changed after that, got angrier,
know what I mean?' Elizabeth knew precisely

5

what he meant. She stared at the painting and
saw Damian's face imposed on it; a hard,
unsmiling mask with wildness in the black eyes.
When he looked like that Damian frightened her,
that was why she had tried to forget him, put the
Atlantic Ocean between them. It was so long
since she had seen him, yet it seemed only
yesterday she had watched him paint that picture;
time telescoped and elongated, it made her feel
dizzy. She hadn't seen him for two years, yet she
felt him present at the back of her mind, she
couldn't evict him from her thoughts and she
didn't believe *he* had forgotten her. Sometimes
she woke up in the night and knew he was
thinking about her. It was a strange experience,
as if Damian was reaching out to her across the
world, it made her sit up in bed trembling. That
was why she hadn't dared to go home to England;
she had wanted to keep as much distance between
them as she could, she was always afraid Damian
would turn up in New York. She hadn't told him
she was going to the States and her family were
sworn to secrecy, they wouldn't tell him if he
came looking for her, but you never knew how
long a secret could be kept. People would hear
she was working in New York and one day
someone might tell Damian.

'A tragedy,' the man beside her said.

Elizabeth hadn't heard the earlier remarks, she
just caught those two words. 'What was?' she
asked absently, turning back to him with a polite
smile.

'His death,' he said, and she just stared, going
cold.

'Whose?' Her voice was raw, she couldn't believe he meant Damian.

'Hayes,' the man said, scowling. 'You weren't listening.' She had wounded his vanity, he wasn't interested in Damian now, he was looking at her with irritation. Men usually looked at Elizabeth in quite another way, their eyes moving from her cool, oval face to the swept-back blonde hair, the supple sway of her body, a distinct curiosity in the way they looked back to her green eyes as if searching for the answer to some question.

'He isn't dead,' Elizabeth said huskily. He couldn't be, it had to be a mistake. 'You must be thinking of someone else—he's only thirty-five!'

'He was killed in a car crash, some time last year. I saw it in the papers, there was a paragraph about it—he'd only just had a big exhibition in Paris, his new style had been quite a sensation. It was a tragic waste, he might have become a great painter.' The man glanced back at the painting and sighed, shaking his head.

Elizabeth's skin was icy. She swallowed and it hurt, her throat was dry and ached. It couldn't be true, she struggled to believe it and couldn't. Damian had been too alive, how could he have been killed without her knowing? How many times over the past year had she thought about him, dreamt about him, felt him present? He couldn't be dead!

She stared unseeingly across the room, her face white. A man standing with a group of guests watched her for a moment, then detached himself. Elizabeth's sight had blurred, she wasn't crying but her eyes were misty. It wasn't until

Max halted in front of her that she noticed him approaching.

'Anything wrong, Liz? You look like a sleepwalker, aren't you feeling too good?' Max sounded anxious and she focused on him with a start.

'Oh, hello, Max.' She forced a smile, but it quivered around her mouth, it didn't fool Max.

He looked at the man beside her. 'Enjoying the party, Greenheim?' There was a touch of aggression in the question, Max no doubt thought her expression was due to something the other had said to her.

'Sure, terrific,' Mr Greenheim said, looking alarmed. Max Adams was a very important man, a rich man already but intending to be richer, a man in a hurry, going somewhere and knowing precisely where he was going. Stockily built, with crisp russet-coloured hair and dark brown eyes, Max moved and spoke with pugnacity. His textile firm was growing like a mushroom, largely through his determination to succeed, and Elizabeth had had her own part in that success. It had been her designs which had been so wildly popular that they had sold like hot cakes. Elizabeth created designs which were fresh and young and elegant; classy stuff, Max had said the first time he looked at her portfolio. Stylish, he had added, nodding that bullet head of his. When you met Max you thought he was formidable, someone to reckon with, but Elizabeth had learnt that under that daunting exterior was a heart of pure gold, especially where she was concerned. He couldn't make enough fuss of her, he didn't want her being tempted away by any of his rivals, he kept her happy; paid her a very high salary, gave her a car, found her a pleasant Manhattan apartment only fifteen blocks from the office and persuaded her to keep fit by jogging with him each morning in Central Park before work. Max had an organising mind, he thought of every tiny detail, and he was protective, he cherished her. He scowled at the worried Mr Greenheim.

'What's wrong, Liz?' he repeated, looking back at her.

'It's so hot in here,' she said huskily. 'Too many people.' She wanted to be alone, she was wondering how she could find out if it was true. If her parents had heard, they would have told her. Who could she ring to ask if Damian was . . . She broke off that sentence, she couldn't even bring herself to say the word. He couldn't be dead, it wasn't possible.

'Okay, I'll take you home,' said Max, putting his arm around her. 'Excuse us, Greenheim, get yourself another drink.' This was Max's party, his apartment; a spacious seven-roomed apartment at the top of a skyscraper block with a view of New York which looked like an aerial photograph, grey and geometric except for the fuzzy green of Central Park which made a splash of colour in the centre. Max had got in an interior decorator whose taste was modern and functional. Chairs could be sat on with comfort, carpets were soft and deep, colours muted and reassuring. You could live in the place, as Max had said appreciatively when he first saw it. He was a very practical man.

On their way to the door they got stopped several times. Elizabeth had trouble controlling her temper, she wanted to get away so badly, she couldn't make polite small talk, and Max noticed, he detached them with firm courtesy.

In the lift, she leaned on the wall with her eyes shut, feeling like death. Max watched her and said nothing.

She opened her eyes and they were whizzing past the twelfth floor. She stared at the illuminated board as if watching a bingo game. 'When did you buy that Damian Hayes?' she asked without looking at Max.

There was a pause before he answered and his voice was thoughtful. 'A couple of weeks ago on that trip to London I saw it in a gallery window. Like it?'

'Yes,' she said, thinking: I liked it when he painted it, I watched each brush stroke going on, I remember every movement he made. He can't be dead, it isn't true. And she waited for Max to say something, to make a remark about Damian. Surely if Damian was dead he would have been told when he bought the picture? She couldn't ask him, she couldn't force the question out, it would make it all too real, and maybe she didn't want to be told it was true, maybe she preferred to live in doubt.

'It's sort of calming,' said Max.

'Yes.' Damian had been relaxed and calm that day he began it, his dark eyes had smiled, his mouth warmly curving. That had been a halcyon spell, by the river, under the trees, with the gentle ripple of water beside them and the air sleepy, they had both been happy. It hadn't lasted, but the memory of it had, and the picture brought it all back. She ached with grief as she thought about it.

'I'd like to buy some more of this stuff,' Max said. 'They had another one, very different, I didn't take to it at all. He'd changed his style, they said. I said: he'd have done better to stick with what he'd been doing.' He laughed and Elizabeth looked round at him in shock, because laughter seemed out of place, it startled her.

'What's funny?' she asked.

'I was remembering the face of the guy in the art gallery, he looked as if I'd blasphemed. I got the feeling I might be buying a picture, but that didn't give me the right to an opinion.' Max sobered. 'Still, I guess he was right. Hayes certainly had a lot of talent, he might have done some terrific work one day.' He broke off, moving, as Elizabeth swayed back against the wall. 'Hey, you aren't going to faint, are you? Liz, what the hell's wrong?'

'Nothing,' she said through stiff lips. 'Tired, I suppose. It's been a long season, now the show's over I think I might take a vacation.' She looked at Max. 'He . . . was in a car crash, wasn't he?'

Max looked bewildered. 'Who? What are you talking about?' He frowned. 'Oh, Hayes, you mean? So they told me—pity, he was good. Look, Liz, why don't you fly on down to my beach cottage at Miami for a few weeks? You need a long rest, I'd say. I hadn't noticed how tired you were, but you look wiped out.'

'I'd rather go back to England for a month,'

she said. 'I haven't been home for two years. I'm feeling homesick, I'd like to see my family.'

Max looked at her sharply. 'Sure, if that's what you want,' he said, but he didn't like it. 'You'll come back, though, won't you? I don't want you staying over there, I need you here. Your contract still has two years to run, remember.'

She forced a smile. 'I hadn't forgotten. I'll come back.'

'Make sure you do.' Max put an arm round her shoulders as they walked out of the lift in the underground car park and made their way to his car. He was a big man, not heavy on his feet, quick moving and graceful for his height. He had a comforting strength, and Elizabeth felt like turning her face into his broad shoulder and crying, but she didn't, she walked steadily and with a white face to the car and Max gently slid her into the seat as though she were made of porcelain.

When he joined her a moment later, he said without looking at her: 'I couldn't manage without you, honey, you know that. You're the best thing that's happened to me in a hundred years.' Before she could respond he had started the car, a flush on his face. Max found emotion slightly alarming, it was a weakness. He did not want anyone to think he had any weaknesses. He had been married and was now expensively divorced and paying pretty hefty alimony to a very beautiful and rapacious redhead who lived in California and had a succession of tanned young men passing through her life. Max was against marriage, he said he couldn't afford it, any more alimony and he'd be bankrupt. He was thirty-nine and wedded to his firm, which didn't stop him looking at women, of course, but none of his relationships had ever become serious, Max made sure of that. He treated women like butterflies flitting through his garden, he watched them with a smile, occasionally trapped one and played with it, but always let them go before *they* trapped him. Elizabeth knew he liked her, she often found him watching her, but she had never given him any encouragement, and their relationship had stayed as a mixture of business and paternalism. It suited her, and she suspected, it probably suited Max, too.

As he drove her through the half-empty New York streets, he said: 'When do you think you'll be going?'

'When can you spare me?'

'Now's as good a time as any, you'll have to start work on next season's designs in a month or so, but until then you won't be seriously missed.' He grinned sideways at her. 'So long as you come back in good time to start work before August.'

'I will,' she promised, and he drew up outside her apartment block, turning her way with an arm along the back of the seat.

'You'd better—if you don't materialise, I'll come and look for you. I need those designs, Liz.'

She smiled and got out. 'Goodnight, Max.'

'Sleep tight,' he said, and the car shot away as she walked across the sidewalk. The air was sweltering after another long, hot day; the towering city rose around her in canyoned density, the tops of skyscrapers hitting the clouds among the smoky orange glow of reflected street lamps.

Elizabeth felt the pressure of all those other people weighing down on her. She loved New York, she had spent an exhilarating two years working there, but tonight she was sad and tired; she suddenly longed for home, for the quiet fields stretching behind her family house in Suffolk, where the only sounds were the wail of the wind in the trees and the distant murmur of the sea.

As she let herself into her apartment she heard the two girls in the next apartment talking loudly and, above their voices, the sound of a radio playing late-night music, while from the floor above came the rattle of machine-gun fire as someone watched a movie on TV. It was a very noisy block at night, and there was no point in complaining, nobody took any notice, in fact if you said anything they were likely to turn up the volume.

Elizabeth made herself some hot milk, got undressed, showered quickly and climbed into bed. It wasn't long before she put out the light, but she did not sleep, she lay in the dark thinking about Damian, her eyes hot, aching with unshed tears. She still couldn't believe it: he was too vital, too fully alive—how could he be dead? When someone dies they vanish, she thought, but Damian hadn't vanished, he had been in her mind all year. It couldn't be true, there must be some mistake.

She woke up early next morning, sweating and shaking, having dreamt about Damian. It had been a confused, incoherent dream of flight and pursuit through shadowy trees and endless echoing rooms in a place she did not recognise. There had been people everywhere, strangers, who stared and whispered as she fled, but wherever she ran she found Damian waiting for her, and at the sight of him her heart would hurt and she would begin to tremble, with fear and with desire, before running again from that dark face, the threat of those intent eyes. Once she had been briefly in his arms on the grass under the trees, his lips on her throat, his hands sliding over her thighs, and she had been moaning, her body so sensitive to his lightest touch that she had felt she was dying. She was pulsating light, a wild erotic beat like the throb of a drum sounded in her ears, she had felt herself give way, yield, surrender herself without inhibitions or conditions, only to find at that instant that she was running again and aware of desperation, a fierce need to find him. The whispers had grown louder, she had caught a few words. 'He's dead, you know,' someone said, and someone else laughed. 'She'll never find him now.' It was at that point that Elizabeth screamed and woke, sitting up in bed, her face dewed with cold sweat.

She slid out of bed, stumbling slightly, and went into the bathroom to wash, her skin felt sticky and her long blonde hair was tangled. In the mirror she looked at herself later with bitterness. Her wet hair was plastered to her scalp, her face was pale and damp. She had spent the last two years hiding from Damian, now she would give anything to see him and it was too late. Life had a weird sense of humour.

Two days later, Max saw her off at Kennedy Airport, pushing piles of magazines into her arms at the barrier, kissing her, repeating again: 'If you aren't back in a month I'll be over there to look for you,' as she turned to walk away. Elizabeth waved to him before she disappeared, but during the long flight over the Atlantic she stared out of the window and thought about her family.

Would they have altered much? Two years wasn't long, yet she knew that she had changed in that time, both outwardly and inwardly. She wore her hair longer, her skin was tanned and clear because she spent a lot of her leisure time at the beach, she had lost weight, her figure was much better and her clothes were very chic. Max insisted that she look good—he had set up a charge account for her with one of New York's top boutiques. Max said she was a walking advertisement for the firm. Why would anyone buy their designs if their top designer didn't look terrific?

She had changed so much, but she hoped her family hadn't changed; she wanted them, childishly, to be exactly the same, to be the people she remembered.

Below the plane floated icebergs of glittering white clouds, with the sun shining behind them, and between them the deep blue of the sky; limitless and unfathomable. Staring out, she could not stop her mind from drifting back to Damian.

She had always thought of him as unfathomable, too. He had disturbed and puzzled her from the moment they met, but although she had never felt quite easy about him she had been fascinated, she had spent long hours thinking about him.

She had known his name before she met him, of course; not merely because she knew his work, which most people in the art world knew by then, but because she had heard of him from an aunt who lived in the same district of the Loire Valley. It was a clannish, close little community, and Damian was the most famous person who lived there. Aunt Fleur had often mentioned him, she was proud of living in the same village.

Elizabeth met Damian in Paris, though, at a party given by one of her lecturers. She was studying art and she was twenty-one, and from the minute he walked into the crowded room she hadn't taken her eyes off him. It had taken her half an hour to find someone to introduce her. She confessed that to Damian later and he had laughed and said: 'You needn't have bothered, I saw you across the room and I had every intention of meeting you, I'd have come over if you hadn't come to me.'

She hadn't believed him, she knew she was nothing special, a skinny young girl with a blonde ponytail and feverishly bright green eyes in a face innocent of make-up. She had only been wearing shabby jeans and a skintight sweater, she looked like every other girl in her year at art college. Damian had been wearing a sweater, too, but it had had French chic, a smooth olive green cashmere which clung to his lean body. He looked terrific. In that noisy room crowded with people busy trying to make an impression, he had

breathed an air of fiercely individual impact.
Everyone looked at him, people tried to listen to
what he said. Impatient, abrupt, he dominated
whoever he was with, and Elizabeth fell head
over heels in love at first sight.

Damian had looked amused when she started
talking about art. 'Live first, paint later,' he
mocked, and took her back to his room that
night. 'Art is tactile,' he said, his strong hands
touching her as though she were a sensuous
object, not a woman; a thing he wanted to
discover, explore, possess and enjoy. She had
been alarmed and worried.

'I'm not going to bed with you,' she had
stammered, very flushed, wondering if she was
going to have a fight on her hands. 'We've only
just met.'

Damian hadn't insisted, he had gone on
caressing her, kissing her, and her body had
turned to a warm, plastic mouldable thing in his
hands, she had been almost hypnotised by the
new discoveries about herself which he was
revealing to her. She had loved him too much,
and it is a mistake to love too much. Damian's
love had been partial, flawed; too obsessive to be
whole because he expected betrayal from the
start. He pushed down all her objections about
going to bed with him, and then distrusted her—
if she could yield to him she would yield to
others; he saw betrayal where none existed. That
was when the dark streak in Damian surfaced and
took him over. Elizabeth learnt to be terrified of
the darkness in him, she couldn't cope with his
violence, and in the end she ran away, but it had

cost her a great deal to leave him, and she still bled from the wound.

It was late in the afternoon when the plane touched down; London looked cool and misty, and Elizabeth shivered at the change after the overwhelming heat in New York. She was only wearing a thin linen suit; she wished she had put on a sweater, too. It was half an hour before she had cleared Customs and there was a long queue for taxis. By the time she drove up to her brother's house she felt exhausted. David worked in the accounts department of an oil company based in London, his hours were long but his salary was high and he had a very attractive home, a converted mews cottage in Islington. The taxi driver cursed as he drove over the cobbled yard and halted outside the little blue-and-white house, which had windowboxes on both floors, in which deep blue lobelia and rose geraniums grew.

The door was flung open as soon as the taxi stopped and David's wife, Helen, appeared, a baby in her arms, smiling. 'You've arrived,' she said, as Elizabeth got out. 'Have a good flight? How does it feel to be back home? Heavens, aren't you brown?'

'Hallo, Helen, lovely to see you,' Elizabeth said, paying the taxi driver as he straightened from dumping her cases on the doorstep. The man nodded and got back into his cab. Elizabeth picked up her cases and staggered with them into the tiny hall.

'Leave them there, David will take them up when he gets home,' said Helen. She was only five foot, with curly gold-brown hair and warm laughing eyes which changed colour according to her mood: now green, now blue, now yellow.

'Is that Greta?' asked Elizabeth, looking at the baby which was gnawing its own fist petulantly and grizzling in a muted way.

'Who did you think it was?' Helen held the baby out and it wailed, clutching at its mother in desperation. 'Come on, take her, she doesn't bite—well, not often, and she hasn't any teeth yet, so she doesn't do you any harm if she does.'

'I can't believe it,' said Elizabeth, taking the baby gingerly. Greta smelt of talcum powder and milk, her body was boneless and warm and she stared up with round, angry blue eyes, her mouth open and all her toothless gums displayed. 'Isn't she beautiful?' Elizabeth said, trying to see some likeness to her brother in that crumpled rose-leaf of a face and failing lamentably. 'She looks like you,' she said, and Helen looked offended.

'I think she looks like David, she's got his nose and chin.'

'Poor mite, how unkind!' Elizabeth teased, and Helen laughed, bridling.

'Can't you see it? Everyone thinks she's like him. Come and sit down, I'll get the kettle on—are you dying for some real tea? The only time I was in New York I couldn't drink the tea, they make it with China tea and it tastes like stewed sawdust, as colourless as dishwater.'

'I drink my tea with lemon over there,' said Elizabeth, following her into the minute kitchen and sitting down at the table with the baby. Greta was busy trying to eat one of the buttons on

Elizabeth's suit. Noticing, Helen clicked her tongue and removed the baby.

'I'll put her in her pram, she's due for a nap, I just fed her.' She vanished and came back, empty-handed, to make the tea.

'David's going to try to get home early,' she promised. 'He's looking forward to seeing you. Tell me all about New York—oh, you're so lucky, living over there, it must be fabulous!' She looked around the room with satisfaction. 'Not that I'd swap, mind you,' she said hastily. 'I've got what I want, but it's nice to hear what other people are doing, isn't it?'

Elizabeth looked at her and envied her. There was egg yolk on Helen's collar and her hair was unstyled, dishevelled, her green dress was one Elizabeth remembered seeing her wearing two years ago, it had been washed until it faded. She looked faintly harassed but happy; her eyes were bright and she smiled all the time.

'I do enjoy reading your letters, Elizabeth,' she said. 'Max sounds terrific, a real ball of fire. David keeps saying you'll end up marrying him, you talk about him so much.'

'Not on your life, we're not that way at all. Max would be horrified if he heard you, believe me.'

'Is he married already?'

'Worse, he pays alimony. Max couldn't afford to marry again.'

'Poor Max,' said Helen, sounding appalled. 'But you do like him, though?'

'I love him, he's wonderful to work for, but to marry? No way.'

'You've acquired an American accent,' Helen said, her tone slightly reproving.

'Have I?' Elizabeth was surprised, she hadn't noticed herself sounding American, but maybe after two years she had picked up the odd intonation here and there, it wouldn't be surprising if she had.

'How long are you staying?' asked Helen, and Elizabeth laughed.

'Hoping to get rid of me already?'

'Don't be silly, we're all delighted to have you back. I just wondered if you planned to come home for good or . . .'

'I have another year to run over there—this is just a holiday.' Elizabeth broke off as she heard a key being inserted into the lock of the front door.

'David's home!' said Helen, her face lighting up, and got up to meet him. David kissed her as he came through the door. 'She's here, she got here safely,' Helen told him, hugging him. They had been married just over two years, but they still behaved like honeymooners, Elizabeth thought, watching them. She remembered her parents being slightly dubious when David told them he was getting married. He had only known Helen a month, his parents had been taken aback at the speed with which he had taken the decision.

'Helen's only nineteen, why not wait a year?' their father had queried, and David had shaken his head, his face determined.

'I know now, what difference does her age make? On paper she may be nineteen, but inside her head she's an adult and that's what counts. Why wait when we're sure now?'

David had only been twenty-four himself, but he had looked older as he argued with their parents, and obviously the marriage had worked, they both looked very happy.

'Hi,' said Elizabeth as her brother turned to her, smiling.

'You look wonderful, it's good to see you,' David said, kissing her. 'You certainly look better than when I last saw you.'

Elizabeth's smile faded and Helen took her husband's arm in a reproachful grip, scowling at him, her eyes full of meaning. 'Look at that tan,' she said quickly. 'I keep trying to work out how she got that in New York.'

They talked about America for most of the evening, but it wasn't until much later that Elizabeth was alone with her brother while Helen fed the baby upstairs, and she could ask him: 'Had you heard that Damian was dead?'

David looked at her sharply. 'How did you hear that?'

'Never mind that, so you did know? Why didn't you tell me?'

'You never mentioned him in your letters, and I didn't want to dredge up the past, I thought it was best if you forgot all about him.'

Elizabeth looked at the bars of the electric fire. The London streets outside were cold and grey, she felt as though she had come home in winter. Shivering, she asked: 'How did it happen, the accident? Do you know?'

'A car crash over in France—I saw a tiny piece about it in the papers, it didn't give any details, but it did say he was being buried over there.'

'At Flamboise?'

'Yes,' said David. 'Funny name, what does it mean?'

'In the autumn the woods look as if they're on fire,' Elizabeth said, her eyes fixed and unseeing. 'All the leaves go red and orange—it's a fabulous sight, Damian painted it several times. He lived in an old tower by the river with woods right behind it, very isolated, a perfect place for a painter to live. He could paint all day without being disturbed by another living soul.'

'Sounds lonely to me.'

'Damian liked being alone.' Elizabeth felt a cold shiver run down her back. 'I'm tired,' she said. 'I think I'll go to bed now, it's been a long day. I hate flying, especially that Atlantic flight, it seems to go on for ever.' She got up and David watched her, frowning.

'Are you okay, Liz?'

'I'm fine,' she said. 'Just tired.' She smiled at him with an effort. 'Goodnight, it's great to be back home.'

'Great to have you back. The parents are over the moon, they can't wait to see you. I've promised to drive us all down there on Saturday, remember, so have a rest while you can. Don't let Helen drag you out all day tomorrow. She seems to go for long walks with Greta every day, she says pushing a pram is better than jogging.'

'She looks good on it, whatever she does,' Elizabeth said as she went out. She put her head round Greta's door and found Helen just tucking the baby back into her cot. Helen put a finger to her lips and Elizabeth smiled and gave her a wave before going into her own room. All the bedrooms were tiny with dark wooden beams embedded in the ceiling, and the floorboards squeaked as she walked about. She undressed and got into bed, turning out the light immediately. She fell asleep at once and dreamt about Damian. She kept seeing him at a distance and following him, calling his name, but he didn't turn, he didn't look at her, he walked away without seeming aware of her.

That weekend they drove to Suffolk, Elizabeth sitting in the passenger seat next to David while Helen sat in the back with the baby. Greta conveniently slept for most of the journey, but by the time they arrived at the cottage she was making impatient noises and clamouring for food while Helen tried to soothe her by offering her toys she made it clear she did not want.

'Awkward little brat,' David observed over his shoulder as his daughter flung a rattle away with a disgusted wail.

'She's hungry.' Helen unstrapped her as the car halted outside the cottage and picked her up. 'All right, madam, food's on its way.'

'I'll bring her case,' said David as he got out of the car and went round to the boot. Greta travelled in style, with her own large case of necessities; nappies, bottles, bowls and changes of clothing. Elizabeth watched with a smile as her brother carried it into the cottage.

'Liz! I thought I heard the car, I was at the back feeding the hens.' Her mother hurried down the path and hugged her, stood back to look at her closely. 'You look very smart—what a pretty dress. Aren't you brown? Have you been on holiday? I was so excited when we got your cable—well, we both were, your father was beside himself. He's just driven down to the village to get some shopping for me, he won't be long. Come in, don't stand out here. Oh, it is good to have you back with us! Two years is too long— why didn't you come home last year? But you're here now and you look so well, America obviously suits you.'

They were in the large, sunlit kitchen by the time Mrs Gardiner stopped her breathless sentences and Elizabeth looked around her with contentment. On the broad windowsill slept the family cat, Samson, an enormous ginger cat with a white tip to his tail. He ignored the invasion of his kitchen, but the tip of his tail stirred and one eye lifted infinitesimally as he checked to see who had arrived, but secretly. Samson was a very cautious cat, but lethal once he had laid his plans. No mouse ever dared to twitch a whisker inside the house while Samson was around.

'Let me look at you,' Mrs Gardiner said after she had put the kettle on.

'No, let me look at you, you've already had a good look at me,' Elizabeth teased, smiling. Her mother looked the same. Perhaps a few more grey hairs, a few more lines on her suntanned skin, but her thin wry face looked just the same, her grey eyes were as sharp and shrewd, her mouth as gentle. Mrs Gardiner was a happy woman, she loved living in the old weatherboard house on the edge of a Suffolk village, with a windswept garden and a view of the sea from the upstairs rooms, she loved her husband and her children even though she worried about them from time to time, her days were full. She gardened, cooked, made patchwork cushions and quilts to be sold at the local church jumble sales, did her shopping in the village and called on her friends for coffee or tea.

'Imagine you living in New York,' she said. 'The world's shrinking every day. I didn't even go to London until I was thirty and then I thought I was living an exciting life, I can tell you, and here are you flying back and forth across the Atlantic without a second thought. It's amazing!'

'You and Dad must come to New York to see me,' Elizabeth told her, and her mother glowed, going pink.

'All that way? It would cost the earth, we couldn't afford it. We're not made of money, you know.'

'I could . . .' Elizabeth began, and Mrs Gardiner stopped her.

'No, I'm too old to start flying. I prefer to stay on the ground, it's safer.' She began to make the tea. 'Helen's just feeding baby, she'll be down in a minute. Oh, there's your father's car—run out and meet him, Liz, he's dying to see you.'

Tactful, Elizabeth thought, as she went back into the garden. Her father was just opening the gate. He stopped as he saw her, his arms full of packages and paper bags. 'Liz!'

'Hallo, Dad.' She put both arms round him, packages and all, and kissed him, standing slightly on tiptoe. John Gardiner was over six foot, a long, rangy man with a lazy way of walking and talking. His hair was iron grey now, but it had once been black. His eyes held warmth as he smiled at her, and she thought how like David those eyes were, still a deep blue, still open and lively and full of interest. John Gardiner met life with curiosity and speculation, he was interested in everything from caterpillars to the internal workings of the combustion engine. His quizzical attitude to life kept his mind young. He was far readier to admit new ideas than his wife, who rarely budged from her own small territory and her own familiar habits.

'How does it feel to be home? Does it all look smaller and paler? New York must be very different, but I can tell you love it from the way you write.'

'I'm having a terrific time, Dad. Every day is exciting.'

'And your boss? Is he exciting?'

She made a face at him. 'Helen warned me you'd been matchmaking.'

'Such a thought never crossed my mind,' he said, laughing.

'Well, that's good, because you'd be way off course. Max and I are not interested in each other that way, so forget it.'

Her father juggled with his packages and she took some of them from him. As they walked to the house, John Gardiner asked: 'And Damian? How do you feel about him now?'

Elizabeth looked at him quickly. 'Haven't you heard? But . . .'

'You know?' Her father frowned. 'Did David tell you?'

'No, I heard from someone in New York. Dad, why didn't you let me know?'

'We felt the best thing for you was to forget him. He gave you a bad time, Liz. It was a terrible thing, that accident, but as far as you were concerned, we didn't want to upset you all over again. Damian Hayes was well out of your life. Keep it that way.' Her father halted to look down at her soberly. 'I don't want to sound hard, but . . .'

'I know,' said Elizabeth, her face colourless.

Her father looked searchingly at her, his brows drawn. 'You . . . don't still feel . . . anything for him, do you, Liz?'

'I don't know what I feel,' she said, and went into the house. She found Helen and David with Mrs Gardiner; sitting around the old, scrubbed deal table in the centre of the kitchen. A glass vase of flowers glowed in the middle of the table, paeonies, roses, blue spikes of delphiniums. A plate of home-made scones, a large rich fruit cake and some strawberries in a china bowl were arranged around the vase and Mrs Gardiner was pouring tea into the fluted cups which Elizabeth remembered so well, their white glaze painted with tiny pink roses. For the first time she felt she was home, she was really home, and then she asked: 'But where's Vicky?'

'She's staying with a friend from college, but she'll be home tomorrow,' her mother answered, passing her a cup.

'You won't know her,' said John Gardiner. 'She's so grown up she frightens me.'

'The only thing that frightens you is work,' his wife said. 'After tea you might mow that lawn—if any of us go out there now we'll need to take a compass, the grass is up to my ears!'

'Why do you exaggerate?' Mr Gardiner spooned jam on to his scone.

'And offer Liz the scones before you eat them all,' Mrs Gardiner scolded.

Drily, Mr Gardiner obeyed, and Liz smiled at him as she took one.

'Greta's cheeks are red—is she teething, Helen?' Mrs Gardiner asked, and Helen eagerly plunged into baby talk.

Mr Gardiner passed the jam to David. 'Seen the latest cricket score? Feeble isn't the word— they've forgotten how to hit the damned ball, if you ask me . . .'

Elizabeth felt the warmth of sunlight on her cheek. How ordinary, how familiar, it all was, and how far away from her hectic life in New York, she couldn't believe she was there one minute; and the next she couldn't remember what it felt like to push your way along the crowded sidewalks between concrete canyon walls with police whistles and car horns blaring all around you.

She fell asleep instantly that night, but in the early hours she woke up with a hoarse cry and sat up, shuddering from a confused dream of Damian. She had been with him, her mind's eye still saw him: a starkly modelled face, the angle of the cheekbones high and fierce, brown flesh drawn tightly over them, emphasising the wildness of those dark eyes, the swooping, sardonic line of the brows. Damian's face was unforgettable, it held an untamed compulsion in it. She had never seen a man like him, she knew she never would again, he was one-off, unique; a man who lived by his own laws, a man whose emotions were explosive.

But it was not his face which had frightened her and which now made her tremble, her breathing quick and painful. It was the brooding insistence of those black eyes, it was the sound of his voice saying: 'I'll never let you go. You're mine, if I can't have you nobody else ever will. Do you hear me? Nobody else, ever, I'll never let you go.'

In the half light before dawn she couldn't be sure if he had ever said that to her. It had been so familiar, she had felt she had heard him say it before. It had made her wake up, a scream breaking from her. Now it echoed inside her head: mine, mine, never let you go, never, and Elizabeth's skin was cold with dread.

CHAPTER TWO

VICKY arrived home on Sunday afternoon, just in time to see Helen and David before they drove back to London. She greeted Elizabeth with a hug and an envious stare. 'You look sensational, aren't you chic? It isn't fair!'

Elizabeth laughed, hearing echoes of their childhood squabbles. 'It isn't fair' Vicky had wailed a hundred times a day over everything from Elizabeth's first long party dress to her first date with a blushing, spotty young man aged sixteen who gave Elizabeth her first kiss and bought her a box of chocolates which he then proceeded to eat himself.

Cuddling Greta, Vicky said: 'She's gorgeous, isn't she? I could eat her up.'

Helen anxiously removed her baby before Vicky could do anything of the kind, and David grinned: 'Cannibal!'

Vicky put out her tongue at him and he said: 'I don't envy the guy you marry—you'll make his life hell.'

'Sensuous bliss!' Vicky assured him, flinging herself down on a chair and stretching with her arms above her head; a small, supple and distinctly dangerous blonde cat. 'I know every trick in the book! You'd be amazed how much you learn at a modern university!'

Her brother eyed her with disgust. 'I wouldn't

boast about that if I were you.'

'No, that was very naughty,' Mrs Gardiner agreed.

Helen laughed. 'She's pulling your leg, where's your sense of humour, David? You know Vicky, all talk and no delivery.'

'Who's been ruining my reputation?' Vicky asked.

'We're going,' David announced, getting up. 'Liz, if you want a few days in London any time give us a ring, we'll be glad to have you. You can babysit for us.'

'Oh, joy,' said Vicky to nobody in particular. 'Isn't he gracious? Come and stay, he says, you'll be a useful slave.'

'Shut up,' David told her, collecting Greta's things. 'Ready, Helen?'

'Yes, I'm ready,' said Helen, following him to the door. ''Bye, everyone.'

Vicky made a face at Elizabeth across the room. 'He's got her right where he wants her, well under his thumb. When he gets home from the office his dinner is on the table, his clean shirt is hanging in the wardrobe—Dave's got it made and he knows it.'

'Helen seems rapturously happy to me,' Elizabeth commented.

'That's the really devilish part of it, she's in seventh heaven, poor girl. She can't wait to toil around him day and night, she loves her chains.'

Mr Gardiner winked at Elizabeth. 'Vicky has decided she's a feminist. Any day now she hopes to persuade her mother to fling me out of the house, bag and baggage.'

'Who set Dave his example?' Vicky demanded.

'Your mother,' Mr Gardiner said cheerfully. 'She waited on him from the day he was born, he never even had to do the washing up.'

'That's true,' said Vicky, struck. 'Maybe you should fling Mum out.'

'I'm thinking about it,' her father said, grinning.

'Why don't we put her in her place?' Elizabeth asked, tongue in cheek. 'Why don't we get the supper tonight, that will show her she isn't indispensable.'

'Great idea,' Vicky agreed. 'Let's make spaghetti, I learnt how to do a really luscious sauce from an Italian guy at college. He could make spaghetti that melted in your mouth and his sauces were out of this world; an onion, a tomato and a scrap of bacon and he was well away. He lived really cheaply in his digs and ate like a king. Girls used to queue up for the privilege of dating him.'

'Girls aren't what they used to be,' her father complained. 'They're so mercenary these days.'

'When you're existing on a government grant you soon learn to think practically,' Vicky told him. She struck an attitude, her hand on her hip. 'Any man with the price of a square meal . . .'

'Disgusting!' snorted Mr Gardiner, as his wife came back from seeing David and Helen off.

'What is?' she asked.

'Don't ask,' her husband said. 'It would shock you.'

'I'm not that easily shocked.' She looked at Vicky suspiciously. 'Now what have you been telling your father?'

'Why don't you and Dad go and watch TV? Liz and I are going to make the supper.'

Mrs Gardiner mimed amazement. 'You can't mean it! What are you planning to make? Beans on toast?'

'Never you mind,' said Vicky. 'Boy, you've got a nasty tongue for a lady of your age!'

'I'm not senile yet,' Mrs Gardiner said. 'I'm still able to come over there and box your ears, madam.'

'Come on,' said Mr Gardiner, putting an arm round her. 'Let's get out of the kitchen and leave the girls to work their magic.'

The door closed behind them and Vicky got up, took Mrs Gardiner's apron down from the hook behind the door and tied it round her small waist. She was a diminutive girl, five foot two, perfectly proportioned for her height, her curves emphasised by the very tight jeans she was wearing and the thin cotton T-shirt, bright pink, beneath which her breasts strained. Her blonde hair was tied in two bunches with pink satin bows. 'You look like Shirley Temple,' David had commented disagreeably, and she had made horrible faces at him, but in fact, the style suited her heart-shaped face. Whatever she wore, people noticed her. Vicky was not a wallpaper person.

'How's New York?' she asked, getting out the onions.

'Fine—do you think you've got your degree?'

'Fingers crossed, possibly. I thought the exams were a damn sight easier than I'd thought they would be, they asked questions I could actually answer.'

'Sounds good.'

'It doesn't do to be too hopeful,' Vicky said wryly, and Elizabeth shivered.

'That sounds awful, don't be so pessemistic.'

'Realistic,' said Vicky. 'You know all the proverbs—never count your chickens, never cross your bridges, etc., etc. I worked like a dog last term.' She grinned. 'Making up for all the fun I've had when I should have been slaving at my books! Believe me, I'm dead. I've never worked with so much concentration before—it's exhausting. I don't think I could go through that again, so I hope I have passed.' She finished chopping the onions and began to blanch the tomatoes in a bowl of hot water. 'What I need is a long holiday. I thought I'd write to Aunt Fleur and ask if I could come over to stay for a week—she's always inviting me, I think she gets lonely in that cottage all by herself.'

Elizabeth had begun frying bacon. She paused, fork in hand, and looked out of the window. The sun was setting behind the trees on the horizon, the sky was running with orange flame, a glimmering, glowing light which made the landscape mysterious, a country of dreams.

'I was thinking of going over to see her while I'm back in Europe,' she said.

'Why don't we both go? She has two spare bedrooms. Don't you remember when Mum and Dad first took us over to stay with her? We all stayed there for a fortnight—that was a marvellous holiday, I remember every minute of it.'

Elizabeth was silent and Vicky looked round at her, coming over with the plate of chopped onions and skinned tomato a moment later. 'Would you rather go on your own?' she asked as Elizabeth slid the vegetables into the pan.

'No,' said Elizabeth. 'I'd love to go with you, if Aunt Fleur can have us.'

'We'll have fun,' Vicky said. 'I love the Loire Valley, there's so much to do there. We could hire a car and visit all the chateaux. I've got some savings left.' Vicky had always worked during her vacations and she was very careful to save some of her earnings. Her lively temperament was slightly misleading; she was very disciplined in her attitudes under that bubbly exterior. Elizabeth was quite sure she would have passed her exams, Vicky had always passed exams. As Helen had said, what Vicky said and what Vicky did were two different things. Vicky had soon learnt that if she smiled and talked a blue streak she got plenty of dates; men were attracted to her extrovert façade, and Vicky enjoyed being in demand.

The water was boiling. Elizabeth slid the stiff pieces of spaghetti into the pan and watched them soften and bend. Deftly she coiled them round, and Vicky went over to lay the kitchen table. Over her shoulder she said: 'Dave told me about Damian being killed—that was tough. Sure you want to go back there? I mean, don't let me talk you into it if you're not sure you can handle it.'

'I told you, I already planned to go,' Elizabeth said flatly.

'Well, it's best to lay ghosts,' Vicky murmured, and Elizabeth shuddered, her face turning pale. She was grateful for the fact that her sister had her back to her. It was a minute before she could ask with deceptive lightness: 'Do you believe in them?'

'Ghosts?' asked Vicky, rummaging in the cupboard for the tub of grated Parmesan. 'Not really, if there are any I've never seen them. Do you?'

'No!' Elizabeth said too emphatically, and felt Vicky turning to stare at her. Nervously she plunged into hurried speech to forestall any questions. 'It's all imagination, people's minds play tricks on them. I bet Hamlet only thought he talked to the ghost of his father, he already had his suspicions about his uncle and he wanted someone to confirm them, he wanted to believe he was seeing his father.'

'Guilty conscience,' said Vicky, and Elizabeth started.

'What?'

'Hamlet—he felt guilty about the way he'd really felt about his father, so he had bad dreams about him, that's what I've always thought. All the haunting went on in his own mind.' Elizabeth listened, frowning.

'Isn't it terrifying to think that your own mind can be your enemy?' she thought aloud. 'If someone doesn't like you, it's bad enough, but when your enemy is right inside your own head, what do you do?'

Vicky was gently stirring the sauce, the smell delicious now as all the ingredients combined. Without looking up, she asked: 'Is Damian haunting you, Liz?' using a low, expressionless tone, like someone trying to catch a bird without frightening it.

Elizabeth laughed huskily. 'Smart!'

'Is he? You shouldn't let him, you know. It wasn't your fault. He was a very difficult guy, that jealousy of his was almost pathological. You never gave him cause, did you?' She paused, then looked up, watching her sister's pale face. 'Did you?' she asked with the hint of uncertainty, and Elizabeth shook her head.

'No, there wasn't anyone else. Damian had his enemy in his own head, too. He was convinced that every man I smiled at was my lover, he wouldn't listen to anything I said. His rages blew up out of nowhere, it got to the stage where I was scared of even speaking to a man. I couldn't live with it in the end, it was terrifying.'

'Was he violent?'

'Physically? He hit me once or twice, but no, it wasn't so much that—it was his face, his voice, the way he looked at me, as if he hated me. There's a very thin wall between hate and love, and at times I felt he crossed it.'

'Scary,' Vicky commented. 'This is ready, I'll give the parents a shout.' She went towards the door, then looked back, smiling. 'You did the right thing, walking out on him, you know. Don't feel guilty about it, Liz, it was the only thing you could do. Heaven only knows where it would have ended if you hadn't. Dad told me once that he was very relieved when you went to the States. Damian came here in a black rage, you know, he threatened all sorts of things. Dad said he was appalled when he realised just what you'd been going through.'

'Dad didn't tell me Damian had come here!'

'No, they decided not to tell you.' Vicky grinned at her. 'They were trying to protect you. Sweet, isn't it? Mum was clucking like an old hen, she was sure that if Damian found you he'd strangle you. So don't let yourself brood about it, honey child. Damian was his own worst enemy, you don't have anything to blame yourself for.'

She went out and Elizabeth stared at nothing, her face sombre. Don't I? she thought, and wished she could be sure about that.

Next morning Vicky sent a telegram to Aunt Fleur, who responded immediately with another, saying: 'Delighted have you, come at once, all love to everyone, Fleur.'

Vicky danced about, waving it. 'Yippee, we're going, we're really going! Isn't she a pet?'

'How are you going to get there?' Mr Gardiner asked. 'Fly?'

'First we'll try and book on the cross-Channel ferries, but at this time of year we may have trouble getting on one, so we may have to fly, but that's expensive, and we'll need a car if we're going to get around while we're over there.'

'You can borrow my little car,' Mrs Gardiner offered. 'I rarely use it, I can manage without it for two weeks.'

'You're an angel!' said Vicky, darting over to hug her. 'Well, if we can book on a ferry I'll take you up on that—thank you, for that I'll do the washing up tonight.'

They were able to get a booking on the ferry the following Wednesday. It was raining hard as they drove through Kent very early in the morning. The motorway was deserted, the tarmac black and slippery. Elizabeth drove very carefully, her eyes intently fixed on the road ahead. The windscreen wipers flicked busily, the windows ran with rain.

'Not a very auspicious beginning,' Vicky commented.

'With luck the weather will be better over in France.'

'Let's hope so, otherwise we'll have a rotten holiday. It's no fun sightseeing in the pouring rain.' Vicky grinned at her. 'I bet you wish you'd stayed in the States and gone to Florida instead.'

'No, I was homesick, and it's been wonderful to see the family. I've missed you all.'

It took ages for them to queue up at the docks and drive on to the ferry, and by the time they were able to relax and sit down for breakfast on the ship Elizabeth felt almost too tired to eat, but after a leisurely meal she recovered enough to go up on deck and stare towards the mist-wreathed shoreline of France which was already beginning to appear in the distance. The weather was still stormy, the ship tossed and bucked underneath her feet, the waves were crashing around them and the wind howled like a banshee. Most of the other passengers were staying safely below, few of them had felt like eating breakfast.

It was past noon before they were driving away from Calais. Elizabeth had to concentrate on the road, she took some time to get used to driving on the other side of the road and drove very slowly at first.

'Shall we stop for lunch soon or press on?' she

asked Vicky, who shrugged, leaning back in the passenger seat with her eyes closed.

'I'm not hungry, I think my stomach is still tossing about on that ship.'

'Rough, wasn't it?'

'You can say that again!' Vicky was pale green, her blonde hair clearly sticky with salt from the sea wind although she had combed it just before they left the ship. Her hair was a slightly different shade from Elizabeth's, a warmer, deeper blonde; where Elizabeth's hair was silvery, Vicky's was golden.

Although at first sight there was a vague resemblance between them, most people soon commented on how different they were, both in looks and character. Vicky was outgoing, lively, vibrant. Elizabeth was calmer, more reflective, introverted, but behind that cool exterior she was deeply emotional. Watching her sister out of the corner of her eye as she drove along a quiet stretch of road she sighed. Vicky was lucky, she took life lightly, she did not let herself get snarled up in troubled relationships. Vicky came out with whatever was in her mind and she dealt frankly with people. If she couldn't alter a situation she pushed it to one side. Elizabeth wished she could do that, but she couldn't; her mind clung like a limpet, she couldn't get free even when she tried. If she had had any sense she'd have forgotten Damian entirely. Well, she had tried, she had stayed away from him for two long years, but she hadn't succeeded in escaping him or he wouldn't be in her head now, she wouldn't be seeing his face everywhere she looked, hearing his voice in her dreams, constantly reliving moments they had spent together. Maybe it had been the shock of hearing he was dead, maybe it had been the surprise of seeing that painting hanging in Max's apartment, who knew what triggered off these things? Whatever the cause, Damian had reappeared in the forefront of her mind and he was staying there.

They drove on across Normandy towards the Loire country all afternoon. The bad weather drifted away, the rain and wind vanishing and the sky clearing, becoming a clean washed pale blue which had a fugitive warmth as the sun came out. The autoroute was fast from Calais to Paris and even faster once they were approaching Tours, after which they were into the heavily wooded countryside of the Loire Valley and driving on narrow roads bordered with tall, Lombardy poplars through whose broad leaves the sun filtered, making a shifting pattern on the road. Elizabeth put on sunglasses against the glare; her head was beginning to ache after the long journey.

'Where are we? How much farther?' Vicky asked, shifting in her seat.

'Another half an hour, I'd guess. Hungry?'

'Famished! I think my stomach rejoined the rest of me a few miles back. Why don't we stop and have a Croque Monsieur and a cup of coffee?'

'At the next village,' Elizabeth agreed, and a few minutes later pulled up in a little village square. Vicky groaned as she stumbled out of the car.

'I've got cramp! My legs aren't working properly.'

'It's been a long drive,' Elizabeth agreed. 'There's a snack bar over there; we'll try that, okay?'

'Fine by me, looks okay. You can do the talking, I haven't got my French together yet, it always takes me a day or two to acclimitise.' Vicky massaged her back as they walked towards the small bar outside which sat a sprinkling of locals drinking tiny cups of black coffee. One or two young men were drinking beer, their dark eyes followed Vicky and Elizabeth as the girls walked past.

'*Bonjour, madame,*' Elizabeth said to the woman behind the bar, who nodded.

'*B'jour, madame.*'

The ritual over, Elizabeth asked if they could have a Croque Monsieur each and a large coffee, and the woman nodded again, sparing of words. A few minutes later she came over to their table in the tiny bar and put in front of them a round of toast topped with hot, bubbly cheese in which was embedded little pieces of ham.

'Smells delicious,' Vicky sighed as she began to eat.

The coffee was so strong Elizabeth had to sip it once she had finished her Croque Monsieur and Vicky made faces over it. 'I wish I'd asked for some milk—this stuff is lethal! I'd forgotten how strong French coffee is.'

When they had finished their snack they drove on towards Flamboise, the village where Aunt Fleur lived, their road running between deep

shadowy forests full of waving green fern and
alive with the secret call of birds. It was very late
now; the sun was moving down the sky and the
air thickening. Those winding paths through the
forest were so familiar. Elizabeth had walked
along them with Damian, she had eaten with him
at that auberge they were passing, she remembered sitting out under the trees in the
afternoon sunshine sipping white wine and slowly
eating wild strawberries which came to the table
nestling on carefully arranged ferns. Everywhere
she looked, she was reminded of him, she
couldn't escape him here, she couldn't forget the
past, and perhaps it had been crass stupidity to
come here, for after all, she had known how it
would be; but she had wanted to walk here, see
these haunted familiar places. Until she had faced
the ghost of Damian she would always be aware
of his presence, she would never lay his spirit to
rest. She almost felt that he had been calling her
here, ever since she heard he was dead, or maybe
even before that. How many times during the
past two years had she dreamt about him?
Although she had run away from him she knew
she had never quite freed herself from him, she
had always been uneasily aware that what had
been between them wasn't finished, their troubled
past cast a shadow into the future for her. She
had felt sure somehow that one day they would
meet again, but now he was dead, and it could
never happen, she would never see Damian again,
but however many times she told herself that, she
felt the same wild stab of pain, the same inner cry
of disbelief. She couldn't convince herself, she

couldn't believe it. If Damian was dead, why did he keep calling to her? Why was he haunting her mind? Was it all her fevered imagination? Or had his violent emotion been so strong that even death couldn't end it?

The road to Aunt Fleur's house ran along beside the river, high above the willow-lined banks. In the dusk the air was thick with insects; moths and flies flitting between the branches of murmuring trees, and the sound of the running river came up to them as Elizabeth halted at the crossroads before turning down the left-hand road. Vicky had sagged in her seat again, her head sunk on her chest as she half-slept. Elizabeth was about to move forward again when she saw someone walking along the river bank. Her glance was casual, then she stiffened, drawing a sharp breath, feeling as though someone had just kicked in her ribs.

It couldn't be! She gripped the wheel involuntarily, staring down through the close-set trees. The tall figure appeared and disappeared, moving slowly, in the mothy dusk. She couldn't see his face or his clothes, only briefly catch glimpses of him. He seemed to be wearing dark pants and a black sweater or shirt, his hair blew in the wind as he moved, hiding his face.

She couldn't take her eyes off him, yet her rational mind told her it was crazy. Damian is dead, it can't be Damian, what's the matter with me? Am I going round the bend? I see a man walking on a river bank and suddenly it has to be Damian—that's insane! If only I was closer, could see him properly—why doesn't he look round, then I'd see his face and know for sure.

The man halted, lifted his head to watch a bird winging over the glassy water from one bank to another. The movement was so intensely, movingly familiar. That was how Damian moved, she knew the long, supple line of that back, she knew it was him.

She undid her seat-belt, opened the car door and almost fell out, beginning to run. 'Damian! Damian!'

CHAPTER THREE

'Liz! Where are you going? What is it?' Vicky called behind her, peering out of the car window, but Elizabeth ignored her. Slithering and skidding, she rushed down the wet grassy bank among the brambles and gorse bushes, oblivious to the scratches and grazes she was collecting. Damian had vanished among the willow trees, she couldn't see him now, but she saw the trailing branches moving, as though he had just walked through them, and as she reached the muddy path beside the river she put on speed, her heart racing inside her.

'Damian! Damian, wait!'

She burst through a curtain of green leaves and stopped, trembling, as she saw him standing there, his head turned back towards her. She couldn't see his face, the shadows were too thick under the trees. 'Damian?' she whispered, putting out a hand, then as he turned slowly without speaking she knew, she was certain, and she leapt to meet him, her arms going round him. A wild relief and joy rushed into her and she began to cry, her head on his breathing chest while her hands touched him, absorbed the reality of flesh and bone, the warmth of skin beneath the sweater he was wearing. She heard his heart beating, his lungs taking in air, her hand

traced the familiar, unforgettable curve of his
long spine, she touched his shoulder blades and
felt that muscular strength again. She had her
eyes shut, the tears were crawling under her lids,
but her body was weak with happiness.

Holding his shoulders she lifted her head to
look at him through her tears. His face was a
blank blur of pale flesh, she could distinguish no
features in this light, only see the gleam of dark
eyes. She stood on tiptoe and found his mouth
hungrily. It was cold, stiff; she kissed it
pleadingly again and again. 'Damian, darling—
Damian!' For a few seconds it resisted the touch
of her lips, then she felt it move and her head
spun into dizzy sensual excitement as Damian's
mouth took hers in demanding passion, a
remembered kiss with anger in it; hard, punish-
ing, but erotic, too, with all the power of
obsessive love behind it. It was as it had been;
fire and ice ran through her, she was afraid and
aroused, her whole body pulsing to the bitter
rhythm of his love. Eyes closed, clinging to him,
she heard pounding which grew louder and
louder so that she no longer knew whether it was
inside her head or outside, then Damian pushed
her away and she fell backwards against the
rough trunk of the willow.

Shaking, gasping, she lay against it, her lips hot
and aching from his long kiss, and the pounding
was right beside her, it wasn't in her head at all, it
was the sound of horse's hooves on the river
bank. The next second the horse parted the
willows and she shrank in shock from the sight of
it. Almost instantaneously Vicky arrived. 'Liz,

what on earth are you up to? What are you doing down here?'

The horse had halted, the rider was bending in the saddle to peer at Elizabeth. Dazedly, Elizabeth heard her speaking in French, so fast it was impossible to catch a word, but the questioning in her voice spoke for itself.

Vicky answered the other girl. Elizabeth said: 'Damian,' and then looked round for him. He wasn't there.

'Damian?' she called, straightening from the tree and starting to run. She came through the willow curtain and her eyes flashed quickly along the river bank. There was no sign of him. 'Damian, where are you? Darling, don't go . . .' Her voice held wildness, the edge of hysteria. Where had he gone? She looked up at the road, but he hadn't had time to climb the bank, she looked back at the willow-swept river path and it was empty, no one moved on it.

'Liz, what the hell is it?' Vicky had joined her. Liz looked round at her, eyes wide and glazed.

'Damian—he's gone!'

'Liz!' Vicky exclaimed, staring. She sounded upset, she put her arm round Elizabeth and held her tightly.

'I've got to find him, where has he gone?'

The girl on the horse was standing just behind Vicky, holding the reins in one hand loosely, watching Elizabeth in a strange way. Vicky looked round at her, almost as if begging her to say something.

'Where is he?' Elizabeth demanded again,

looking at the rider. 'You saw him, where did he go?'

'I did not see anyone,' the girl said in slow French. 'Only you, there was only you.' She looked at Vicky. 'And you,' she added. 'There was no man here.'

'There was,' said Elizabeth, but she was shaken, her voice trembled. She looked at Vicky. 'I saw him, I spoke to him, he kissed me—he was here, Vicky. Damian isn't dead, I knew he wasn't, he's alive and he was here!'

'What is she talking about?' asked the French girl, and her horse shifted, its hooves grinding the muddy path, and tossed the flowing black mane in an impatient way, as though eager to be gone.

'We'd better be going,' said Vicky, urging Elizabeth forward. She gave the other girl a quick smile. 'Goodbye.'

'Is she okay?' the French girl asked, she sounded curious and slightly amused, as though she thought Elizabeth wasn't quite right in the head, but then that was often how the French sounded confronted with the English, Elizabeth remembered that all too vividly.

'She'll be fine,' said Vicky, eager to get away.

Elizabeth ignored the other girl, she looked at Vicky. 'I'm not imagining it—I tell you he kissed me, I felt him, you can't imagine something like that. I touched him, Vicky.' She held out her hands, they were trembling, Vicky stared at them and looked anxious. 'I touched him, you've got to believe me!'

Vicky was helping her to climb the bank.

Behind them the other girl stood watching, the
wind blowing her long black hair so that it
mingled with the mane of her horse, the colour
almost indistinguishable. Elizabeth looked back
at the empty river path. He had been there, she
hadn't imagined it, she wasn't going crazy. The
French girl stared up at her, from this distance all
Elizabeth could see of her face was a smooth
whiteness with dark eyes fixed in it.

'She must have seen Damian,' Elizabeth said.
'If she saw me, she must have seen him.'

'She said she hadn't, Liz.'

'She was lying.'

'Why should she? Do you know her? Ever seen
her before?'

'No.' Elizabeth searched her mind. 'No, never,'
she decided.

'You're tired,' said Vicky. 'It's been a long day
and you're worn out. We'll be there in ten
minutes, you can go to bed, you'll feel better
when you've had a good night's sleep.'

'I'm not crazy!' Elizabeth protested. 'Don't
talk to me as though I was.'

'I'm not!'

'Aren't you? I think you are, you think it all
happened in my own head, you don't believe I
saw Damian, that he kissed me, but I know it
was him—when you've just touched someone
you know it isn't all imagination, and I had my
arms round Damian, Vicky—I heard his heart
beating, he was warm and breathing, he was
alive!' She stopped, breathless, and looked at
her sister angrily. 'So don't try to tell me I
imagined it all.'

Vicky sighed. 'Did he talk to you? What did he say to you?'

Elizabeth hesitated, frowning.

'What did he say?' Vicky pressed, watching her.

'He . . . didn't talk, he kissed me.' It sounded lame, even to her. Damian hadn't said a word, she realised, and neither had she, she had been too uptight, her heart had been too full to talk, she had only wanted to touch him and believe that he was alive. Had she imagined it? But that would mean she really was going crazy.

'Come on,' ordered Vicky. 'Get in the car, I'll drive.'

'You can't . . .'

'I know how, I've had lessons, I just don't have a licence yet, but it isn't far and I'll be careful. You're in no state to drive, Liz.'

'I'm all right,' Elizabeth said raggedly. She slid into the driving seat and Vicky slowly got in beside her. Starting the engine, Elizabeth drove on, staring at the road. It was quite dark now, her headlights picked out moths flitting across the road, a rabbit leaping for cover at the sound of her engine. There were no houses in view, and the countryside pressed forward around the road, breathing softly in the night; empty, almost menacing, alien and unknown.

'Maybe I shouldn't have talked you into coming here,' said Vicky, hearing the deep sigh Elizabeth gave, then she pointed. 'There it is, isn't it? That's Aunt Fleur's house, I remember it.'

Without answering Elizabeth slowed and

pulled up. There were lights in the downstairs rooms, a sound of music. It was a small cottage, stone-built, with a smooth grey slate roof in which was set a high, pointed gable window. On the other two floors the windows were flush with the walls, flat, narrow windows which gave the rooms little light, she remembered; it was a shadowy little house.

'It looks smaller than I remember,' said Vicky, leaning forward to stare.

'Things always do.' Elizabeth's voice was as dry as grass in summer bending in the wind, she felt very weary. It had seemed so real at the time, but now she wasn't sure. Had she held Damian, been kissed by him? Or had she conjured him up from her memory because she desperately wanted him to be alive, she couldn't face the thought that he was dead?

The front door opened and a tiny figure appeared framed in yellow light. Vicky jumped out and called, 'Aunt Fleur! We're here!'

'So I see.' Fleur Perret hugged her and kissed her. 'Vicky, I don't believe it, haven't you changed? Only a couple of years and you're suddenly all grown up!'

Vicky was laughing. 'And just about to get my first job, too. I shan't feel grown up until I'm earning.'

'Have you got your degree?'

'I won't know for a few weeks, they take ages to publish the results, but keep your fingers crossed for me. I'm a bundle of nerves. Three years' work . . .'

'I'm sure you'll have passed, your father tells

me you've worked very hard. He's very proud of you.'

Vicky laughed again. 'Is he?' She flushed and looked delighted. 'Do you think so?'

While they were talking, Elizabeth had got out of the car and opened the boot. She pulled out their cases and put them on the ground, closed the boot again.

'Liz dear!' Aunt Fleur smiled as she joined them.

'Hallo, Aunt Fleur.' Elizabeth kissed her, inhaling the remembered scent of verbena. Aunt Fleur's skin was wrinkled and as soft as crêpe, she was always brown, she spent so much time in the open air. She had long ago been absorbed into French life, it was hard to believe she was really English now, even harder to believe that she was their father's sister. She was much older, of course, ten years separated her from her brother, and she had married Jacques Perret when she was just eighteen, more than forty years ago. When her husband died her family had expected her to come back to England, but Fleur Perret had merely laughed at the idea. By then she had spent over thirty years in France and the idea of leaving it had seemed ridiculous to her. France was her home, she had said, she didn't feel English any more, what on earth would she do with herself if she came back?

'You look pale,' said Aunt Fleur, looking at her sharply.

'She's tired,' Vicky said. 'It's been a long drive—we left home at five o'clock this morning, it's been a marathon trip and Liz did all the driving.'

'Come indoors, it's cold out here,' said Aunt Fleur. 'Give me that case, Liz—— no, don't be silly, of course I can manage it. I'm not a geriatric!'

'I'll take it,' Vicky said, firmly removing the case from her.

Talking, Aunt Fleur led them into the house. It was full of the scent of flowers, the rooms were shabbily comfortable, crowded with furniture, pictures, pieces of porcelain and scattered objects left on every available surface without rhyme or reason.

'Have you eaten?' Aunt Fleur asked, and Vicky groaned.

'No, we're starving, but sandwiches will do if . . .'

'I've got some quiche and salad and some nice wild mushroom soup,' Aunt Fleur said, smiling.

'You're an angel, it sounds marvellous!'

'Come up and see your rooms and wash, then when you're ready come down and eat.'

Elizabeth carried her own case into the room she always used. Vicky went into the room next door and Aunt Fleur went with her. Elizabeth heard their voices murmuring. She felt so tired she didn't know if she could eat, she felt grey and drained. She looked into the mirror, her face looked like a sheet with holes poked in it. As she went back to the door to go to the bathroom she heard Vicky's voice speaking softly in the next room. 'Hallucinating?'

'What else could it be?' said Aunt Fleur. 'He's dead, Vicky.'

'Liz sounded so certain.'

'Vicky, Damian was in that car, he was killed only five minutes from this house. I heard the crash, I ran out of here and I saw the flames, the car exploded like a bomb. It had turned over in the ditch, all the petrol had gushed out and it went up, it sounded like the end of the world. Nobody could have lived in that car, he must have died instantly.'

Elizabeth clung on to the door, white-faced, shuddering.

There was a silence, then Vicky said huskily: 'And it was Damian driving it? If the body was . . .'

'Vicky, I saw him drive past, I waved to him. I was just closing the shutters upstairs, I looked out and Damian looked up at me and smiled. I waved, finished closing the shutters and went downstairs. I heard the crash before I got to the bottom of the stairs. I remember it as if it happened yesterday. I stopped dead—you can imagine, I was horrified. I ran to the door and out into the garden and I saw the flames climbing up behind the trees.' Aunt Fleur sighed audibly. 'No, Vicky, it was Damian in that driving seat, and he's dead.'

Again a silence, then Vicky said: 'Then what happened on the river bank just now? I can't believe Liz is making it up, she was too convincing, I believed her. Something happened, she saw someone—if it wasn't Damian, who was it?'

'I told you, my dear, she must have been hallucinating. After all, she was tired, she's under a strain anyway, you told me so yourself, she's just discovered that Damian is dead. Oh, these things happen to the sanest people. The mind plays tricks on us. Haven't you ever been in a house alone at night and been sure you heard someone creeping about upstairs? After Jacques died, I thought I heard strange noises all the time, it was ages before I got used to living alone. When someone close to you dies it leaves you off balance. Liz will recover, a long holiday and she'll be quite normal.'

Elizabeth softly crossed the landing and went into the bathroom. 'Is that you, Liz?' Vicky called, sounding startled.

'I'm just going to have a wash,' Elizabeth called back, closing the bathroom door.

She heard her sister and Fleur going downstairs a moment later. Elizabeth sat on the edge of the bath and covered her face with her hands. Was she going out of her mind? Had she imagined that she saw Damian? She tried to remember how it had felt to be in his arms again, but her mind dissolved, she couldn't be sure it had happened now. Perhaps Vicky and Aunt Fleur were right, perhaps she had suffered a hallucination through being overtired and overwrought.

Over their supper, Aunt Fleur asked: 'How do you like living in New York? Tell me all about it,' and that topic took them easily along for half an hour. Aunt Fleur had a hundred questions to ask about life in America; she had a quick, interested mind and despite living in such an out-of-the-way place she kept an amused eye on what the rest of the world was doing.

Vicky was yawning over their coffee. 'Sorry, I'm dead,' she said, catching Aunt Fleur's eye.

'Off you go to bed, then, both of you. You can sleep as late as you like tomorrow.'

'It's very good of you to have us here,' said Elizabeth, getting up.

'Nonsense, I'm delighted to see you both. I keep trying to persuade your father to come over for a few weeks, but he pleads poverty, can't afford the fare at the moment.'

'Maybe they'll come next summer,' Elizabeth said, and Vicky nodded.

'You could always go to stay with them, Aunt Fleur.'

'Maybe I will.'

In her room, Elizabeth rapidly undressed and got into bed. She was so tired her body was complaining, every limb aching. It seemed a hundred years since they left that morning to drive to Dover. She fell asleep at once and if she dreamt she didn't remember it in the morning. She woke up suddenly and lay, disorientated, for a moment, eyes wide open, looking around the little room and wondering where she was, before she remembered.

Sliding out of bed, she went into the bathroom. There wasn't a sound from the rest of the house and Vicky's door was shut. Elizabeth had a shower and padded back to her own room in her towelling robe, got dressed in casual white jeans and a sleeveless blue cotton shirt.

When she drew back the curtains she found the

garden shrouded in white mist and remembered how often during her visits to the Loire Valley she had woken up to find that a mist had drifted off the river. She stood at the window, brushing her damp hair until it was more or less dry, but the mist didn't lift, although it was almost eight o'clock. She decided to leave her face bare of make-up, her skin felt tight and flushed after her long, deep sleep.

Going downstairs quietly, she found the kitchen empty, but Aunt Fleur must be up, because there were fresh croissants and rolls in the wicker bread bin. Elizabeth ground some coffee beans in the little handmill, the smell of freshly ground coffee was delicious. She suddenly felt very hungry and when the coffee had percolated she sat at the kitchen table eating a croissant and sipping the strong black coffee. For the first time she really felt she was back in France.

There was still no sign of Aunt Fleur. Perhaps she had gone to call on a friend in the village. Should she wake Vicky? Elizabeth hesitated, then decided to let her sister sleep. She slipped upstairs and found an anorak, went back downstairs and out into the mist, which was just beginning to clear. Coils and wreaths of it blew around her as she wandered along the sandy path which ran through a little wood down to the river. The countryside was so flat, so heavily forested, that she always felt hemmed in by trees. This morning the air was cool and damp on her face. There wasn't another soul moving, she was totally alone, except for a squirrel which ran up an oak tree when it saw her, the bushy red tail whisking out of sight among the leaves.

Elizabeth stopped to stare up at it, smiling, then froze as she heard a twig crack among the trees. A few seconds later she saw a movement; someone was walking along a winding path which ran parallel to the path she stood on. She saw a blur of moving limbs, then black hair ruffled by the breeze.

Her heart seemed to have come up into her throat, and she put a hand there, breathing thickly. The sound of whistling came back to her. She knew the tune—it was an old French folk song which Damian had loved and often whistled, a haunting, birdlike melody, high and wistful.

This time it was broad daylight. This time she knew she wasn't imagining it. She saw a man through the trees, and only one man in the world walked in that rapid, loping fashion and only one man whistled like that.

She began to run, bursting through the trees without caring that brambles and thorn bushes clawed and scratched her. The damp ground was littered with leaves which glistened with silvery wetness from the mist, she slipped and caught at a tree trunk, but she kept her eyes on the man walking ahead of her. She would not look away in case he vanished, the way he had last night.

'Damian!' she called, her voice breathless.

He stopped and turned, and from a few feet away Elizabeth saw his face quite clearly, a shaft of sunlight falling on it from above, the gnarled branches meeting overhead like the roof of a

cathedral and the wood shadowy, with bluish
light glancing through the leaves.

She caught her breath in bitter shock. It wasn't
Damian. It was a total stranger—she had never
seen that face before, there was no resemblance at
all apart from the accident of colouring. Black
hair, black eyes, a common enough pigmentation
in France, but where Damian had had olive skin
which usually held a deep tan, this man was pale,
his skin smooth and untouched by wind or sun as
though he rarely stayed out in the open air. His
features were classical, a straight fine nose, thin
brows which had none of Damian's winged and
saturnine mockery, cheekbones which emphasised
the slight hauteur of his stare, gave him a
permanent expression of withdrawal. He looked
cold, controlled, a man whose face gives away
nothing of what is in his mind, yet although she
knew she had never seen that face before she still
felt a strange sense of familiarity, a quiver inside
herself, like the vibration of a harp string after it
has been played.

'Who are you?' she whispered, instinctively
speaking English.

He gave no sign of having understood her. In
French he said: 'You shouldn't be here, madem-
oiselle. This land is private property.' His eyes
had the icy depth of black water, and she shivered
as she met them. His voice was very deep,
slightly hoarse, with a smoky quality, and his
French was rapid, it had the machine-gun fire
sound of the Parisian rather than the more
leisurely drawl of the provincial. Elizabeth could
always manage to understand country people in

France, they spoke slowly enough for her to follow them, but in Paris people rattled out words like bullets.

'I'm sorry,' she stammered. 'I didn't realise.'

'The road is back there, take that path,' he said, gesturing. He still hadn't smiled, she picked up cold hostility in the way those dark eyes watched her.

'Thank you,' she said, about to walk away, when she heard the sound of barking, the scuffle of movements, and through the ferns and bushes crashed two golden dogs, long-haired, silky, their tongues lolling out. They leapt up at the man, their paws on his chest, and he half-smiled, fondling their drooping ears.

Hard on their heels came the black-haired girl Elizabeth had seen last night by the river. This morning she was on foot, her hair swinging loose around her flushed face, her slim figure casually dressed in a pleated tweed skirt in a blue and cream shade, with a deep blue sweater, her waist tightly belted by a wide blue leather belt. Seeing Elizabeth, she halted, her brows drawn, then looked quickly at the man who was still stroking the dogs, whose tails beat excitedly, fanning a little shower of wet leaves into the air each time they whisked over the ground.

'Yves, you shouldn't have walked so far, you'll tire yourself out.' Her voice was anxious, a little scolding, but very careful, as though she didn't dare to be too impatient with him.

'I'm not a child,' he said, looking up.

'You haven't got over your cold, though. You

know Dr Victor told you to stay indoors until it
had quite gone.'

'Don't fuss, Chantal, for God's sake!' he
muttered, frowning.

The girl's mouth trembled. Elizabeth felt sorry
for her, there was no mistaking the way she
watched him, her lustrous dark eyes glowed with
feeling, and although Elizabeth watched intently
she saw no answering feeling in the man's cold
eyes. His face had the untouched impassivity of a
marble statue; those hard, austere features barely
seemed to be made of human flesh and blood.

The girl looked over at Elizabeth, her eyes
unfriendly and hurriedly forcing a smile,
Elizabeth said: 'Hallo again—we met last night,
didn't we? I'm Elizabeth Gardiner, I'm staying
with my aunt, Madame Perret . . .'

'We know who you are,' the man interrupted
tersely, and Elizabeth stared at him, her lips
parted in a little gasp.

'Have we met before?' she faltered, looking
from one to the other of them in questioning
surprise. On her previous visits to Flamboise she
had met almost all the local people, her aunt
knew everyone and Damian had been very much
at home here, but she was sure she hadn't seen
either of them before.

'No,' the girl said in a voice which made it
clear that she didn't want to meet Elizabeth now.
She pushed a hand through the man's arm. 'Let's
walk back, Yves,' she said, turning away from
Elizabeth.

It is never very pleasant to meet hostility.
Elizabeth felt herself flush, she watched them

walk away, the dogs running ahead of them, and angrily turned back towards her aunt's house. What on earth had made her think that that man was Damian? He looked nothing like him, and even in one glance she had been able to see that his nature was utterly different, the man was ice from the feet upward. She felt stupid. It was worrying—was Damian going to be everywhere for her? Would she see him in every dark shadow, every mirror, every man's face? Was that what people meant when they talked about possession, about being haunted? Her own mind was playing tricks on her, she was riddled with guilt over the past. She had to come to terms with the fact that Damian was dead, he was not coming back, it was over. Then, perhaps, Damian would stop haunting her.

CHAPTER FOUR

SHE found Vicky in the kitchen, crouched at the table with a cup of hot chocolate clasped between her hands, still wearing her nightie and dressing-gown, her hair in curly bunches tied with ribbon. She yawned as Elizabeth came in, flapping a hand.

'Hi, early bird. How long have you been up?'

'Hours. I went for a walk. Is Aunt Fleur around?'

Vicky nodded. 'Upstairs.' She yawned again, and Elizabeth laughed.

'Didn't you sleep?'

'Like a log,' Vicky said. She sipped her chocolate, eyes half closed. 'Mmm ... this is terrific, I'd forgotten how good it is to drink hot chocolate for breakfast.'

'Fattening, too,' said Elizabeth, and Vicky made a face at her.

'Who cares? Have you been into the village?'

'No, I walked in the woods.' Elizabeth looked round as Aunt Fleur came into the room with quick, light steps. Tiny, very neat, her grey hair had a natural curl still, her deeply tanned face was finely wrinkled and this morning she was wearing a flowered cotton dress of the type you can buy in any French market; sleeveless, cut on simple lines with a squared neck, it was entirely practical but not exactly chic. It made Aunt Fleur look like a French farmer's wife, she would merge into her background anywhere in the French countryside. Chic clothes were for the Parisienne, not for down-to-earth countrywomen.

'Oh, there you are,' said Aunt Fleur, smiling. 'We wondered what had happened to you.' The words were light, but Elizabeth caught some echo beneath them and her aunt's eyes looked faintly anxious. Elizabeth smiled back at her reassuringly.

'I felt energetic, so I went out exploring.' She paused, then said: 'I ran into some people in the woods—a girl and a man with a couple of dogs, I'd never seen them before. Have they moved here recently? She called him Yves.'

Aunt Fleur's face stiffened. 'Yves?' There was something wary about her now, she watched Elizabeth in an odd way.

'I think he called her Chantal,' Elizabeth added, watching her aunt in turn and wondering why she was staring like that. 'They said they'd heard of me, so I suppose they must know you.'

'What else did they say to you?' Aunt Fleur asked slowly, frowning.

'Told me I was trespassing,' said Elizabeth, shrugging wryly. 'I didn't get the impression they liked strangers much. Who are they, Aunt Fleur?'

'He is Yves de Lavalle, he's from Paris, I think he was in banking. He seems to have plenty of money—he and his wife bought the Château a few months after your last visit.'

'You're kidding?' Vicky exclaimed, laughing. 'That old ruin? It was falling down, all the windows had gone and there wasn't much of a roof.'

Aunt Fleur nodded. 'They still haven't finished the work on it, he must have spent a fortune. It hadn't been lived in for years, of course, but it had a lot of land, including those woods running down to the river. Yves de Lavalle has had the roof timbers entirely replaced, they say, and all the tiles. New windows have been put in, the rooms have been redecorated and he's had bathrooms and a big kitchen installed. Heaven knows what it's all cost, the builders are still there.'

'He must be rolling in money,' said Vicky, fascinated. 'What does he look like, Liz? Is he old?'

'No,' said Elizabeth, suppressing a curious little shiver. 'He's around thirty-five, I suppose, maybe older; rather good-looking, in a chilly way—I felt sorry for his wife, she seemed half scared of him.' It had taken her aback to hear that Chantal was his wife, in fact, there had been an odd atmosphere between them. Had they quarrelled that morning? Or was it just that icy distance in Yves de Lavalle that kept his wife at bay? Suddenly remembering, she looked at Vicky and said: 'She was the girl we saw last night—remember? On the horse?'

Vicky's mouth dropped open. 'That girl? Good heavens!'

'Let's have some coffee,' said Aunt Fleur, getting out the mill and spooning coffee beans into the metal canister. She turned the handle and the smell of roasted coffee filled the air.

Without looking at Elizabeth, she said: 'Yves de Lavalle has only just come home from hospital. Chantal must be very happy to have him back after all these months.'

'What was wrong with him?' Vicky asked curiously, then grinned. 'Apart from being crazy enough to buy that crumbling old place?'

Elizabeth felt her nerves prickle, she sensed something odd about Aunt Fleur's manner.

'He was badly injured, they thought he couldn't live,' Aunt Fleur said. 'He's had half a dozen operations. Chantal has been desperately worried about him, she almost lived at the hospital, it's been a terrible strain on her, poor girl.' She looked round at Elizabeth, her eyes anxious. 'He was in the car with Damian,' she said, and Elizabeth's heart plunged with shocking abruptness. Vicky looked at her too, her face mirroring the same stunned shock.

'You had to know,' Aunt Fleur said uneasily. 'Otherwise if you ran into Yves again you might say something—it was a nightmare for him and poor little Chantal, they hate to talk about it. Yves has been through so much pain, he was on morphine for weeks, they had to wean him off before he became addicted, half the time he didn't recognise Chantal. She looked like a ghost whenever I saw her, everyone was so worried about her, but since Yves began to recover she's much brighter.'

Elizabeth moistened her dry lips before she could speak. 'You didn't tell me Damian wasn't alone when he crashed.'

'It didn't seem to matter, but now you've met

Yves . . . he only bought the Château because of
Damian—it's so ironic. They'd known each other
for years, since college, I think. Yves saw the
Château when he was visiting Damian and fell in
love with it. He'd only just got married, and
Chantal didn't like Paris, she's a country girl, she
loves dogs and horses. Yves had plenty of money,
he decided to move out of Paris, and the Château
was exactly what he and Chantal wanted.' Aunt
Fleur gave a heavy sigh. 'I should think Chantal
often wished she hadn't asked him to move out of
the city.'

'Poor girl,' said Vicky, her face sombre. 'I'd
feel pretty sick in her place, wouldn't you, Liz?'

Elizabeth nodded, her eyes down. 'And she's
crazy about him,' she said huskily. 'I could see
that.' The other girl had not been able to hide
how she felt, she hadn't even tried. Elizabeth had
almost felt Chantal wanted her to notice how
much in love she was, she had taken Yves de
Lavalle's arm possessively. Elizabeth couldn't be
so sure how he felt—there had never been so much
as a gleam of emotion in his cold face, but then if
he had been in hospital for months, suffering
great pain, he might have learnt how to hide what
he felt.

It wasn't until later that day that Elizabeth
remembered what had happened on the riverbank
the night before—had she imagined all of that?
Her mind might be playing tricks on her, but
could it have conjured up so solid a reality? She
had been in a man's arms, he had kissed her, she
could still remember the body warmth against
her, the heat of his mouth. If it had not been

Damian, who ... She shuddered away from that question, flushing angrily. It might be better not to know. What had he thought, whoever it had been?

Vicky had been eager to see one of the famous Loire châteaux, so they had driven to Chinon, where Henry the Second had spent so much time whenever he was in France. The castle was in ruins, but the massive ramparts remained intact, built on a rock above the wide River Vienne during the tenth century, with the busy little town of Chinon behind it at the foot of the craggy hill. Before they climbed up to see the castle, they sat in the town's main square at a pavement café and drank ice-cold chocolate, watching some children playing around the fountain nearby. Vicky and Aunt Fleur were laughing, the sunshine was hot, the sky blue—but Elizabeth felt cold as she remembered how she had clung to a strange man in the dark, and she flushed fiercely as she relived that long kiss, her lips were burning with the memory.

A man walking past their table stopped in his tracks, staring at them, and Elizabeth looked up, her heart thudding. She didn't know him, she had never seen him before, that much her nervous glance told her in a second—then she realised that he was looking at Vicky, not her.

'I don't believe it,' he said, laughing. 'What are you doing here?'

Vicky grinned. 'Small world, isn't it?'

'You didn't say you were coming to France!'

'It was a last-minute decision.'

Vicky was faintly flushed, her eyes suddenly much brighter—Elizabeth had no difficulty picking up the fact that her sister liked this man a lot, and she looked back at him with new eyes, assessing him. He wasn't the type Vicky usually went for—at first sight there wasn't anything special about him at all and Vicky had always been very hard to please where men were concerned.

'Where are you staying?' he asked, glancing at Aunt Fleur and Elizabeth as he spoke, and Vicky hurriedly introduced them.

'Teddy's one of my lecturers,' she explained, as Aunt Fleur smiled at him.

'Teddy what?' Aunt Fleur asked and he shot Vicky a teasing grin.

'Hertford, Madame Perret. Edward Hertford, trust Vicky to skip the boring details. I often wonder what her French and German are like—a lot of very colourful phrases and no grammar, I suspect.'

'As I said, Teddy is one of my lecturers,' said Vicky, groaning. 'Sit down, Teddy, don't *loom*.' She looked at Elizabeth. 'He's good at that, it comes of being six foot two.'

He pulled back a chair and sat. The waiter came over and they all ordered some drinks. 'Been up to the castle yet?' Teddy asked, and Vicky shook her head.

'We were just going up there, it looks like a steep walk. Have you seen it?'

'Several times. I'm staying at a campsite just outside the town.' He smiled politely at Aunt Fleur. 'I travel light—a small tent and the bare minimum of equipment and I can set up home anywhere.'

How old was he? Elizabeth wondered, watching him. Late twenties? He wasn't goodlooking; his face was broad and calm and humorous, almost comical at times with that stubby nose and those large ears. He just wasn't the type she would have expected Vicky to flip over.

'What's your subject?' Aunt Fleur asked, as the waiter brought their glasses of cold citron, and Teddy leaned back, his chair creaking under the weight of his sturdy body. He wasn't bulky but he was muscled, his shoulders wide, his chest deep.

'Botany,' he said, and grinned. 'Don't bother trying to look enthralled, I know most people are bored by botany.'

'Clang!' Vicky said with glee, and he looked from her to Aunt Fleur, who laughed.

'I'm a very keen amateur botanist myself,' she told him.

'Really?' He pushed a mass of very curly brown hair back from his face, looking pleased. 'I'm sort of on a working trip,' he said. 'I always combine holidays with work—maybe you could help me with the local secrets, there are some rare species I haven't tracked down yet.' He patted the camera he was carrying on a cord around his neck. 'I want to get film of all the local flora.'

'Do you take cuttings?' Elizabeth asked, and Vicky whistled under her breath, her face amused.

Teddy looked round at Elizabeth seriously. 'No way. The last thing I'd do,' he said. 'I just record what I see and leave it intact. I'm not in the collecting business, too many of our rare plants are under threat because people don't respect them.'

'He can talk about that for hours,' Vicky warned, and Teddy grimaced.

'Was I being pompous?'

'No more than usual,' said Vicky. She shaded her eyes to look at the sky. 'If you've finished your drink, Liz, I suggest we tackle the climb to the castle before they start locking up.'

They all got up and Aunt Fleur said to Teddy: 'If you get time to visit Flamboise, drop in and see me—I might know of one or two things you'd find interesting.'

'I'd like that,' he said. 'How about tomorrow?'

'Tomorrow would be fine,' said Aunt Fleur. 'Come to lunch.' She told him the address and gave him directions, then they walked away up the flight of steps which led towards the castle.

'He's nice,' Elizabeth said casually to Vicky, who looked at her offhandedly.

'Think so?'

'I liked him very much,' Aunt Fleur agreed.

'He likes older women,' Vicky said, and their aunt burst out laughing.

'Really, Vicky! The things you say!'

Elizabeth watched her sister thoughtfully. 'He isn't married?'

'Not yet,' said Vicky, shrugging. 'But I wouldn't be surprised if he didn't get married soon—he's been seeing a lot of one of the female lecturers, they're a pair, they go everywhere together, have done for a couple of years.

Everyone expects them to marry.' She sounded casual, but Elizabeth was sure she heard something else in her voice. Of course, they were climbing a steep hill, Vicky might just have been breathless because of that, but Elizabeth had a feeling it was more than that.

They reached the clock tower which led to the castle and in which they found a small museum housing relics of Joan of Arc. It had been at Chinon that Joan of Arc first met the Dauphin, although the great hall in which she had seen him, hiding among his courtiers in an attempt to make a fool of her, was no longer there. All that remained of it was an old stone fireplace and a crumbling fragment of one wall. The guide book told them that Chinon was, in fact, three castles in one, although from the river all one could see was a long, creamy façade which seemed to be one castle.

'A lot seems to have happened here,' Vicky commented, as they stood on the wall looking down over the river, watching a red canoe shooting past on the placid water. 'It looks so peaceful, too.'

'Are we going into the Donjon?' Elizabeth asked, consulting their guide-book. 'The Knights Templar were imprisoned there until they were sent to Paris to be burnt at the stake, apparently they did some graffiti on the walls.'

'There are some secret passages under the Donjon,' Aunt Fleur told them. 'Really creepy places, a dark labyrinth, you could get lost down there if you didn't know the way. They tunnelled right down into the rock under the castle.'

'Trying to escape?' Vicky asked, with a delighted shudder. 'Lead me to it—I love secret passages!'

'You've got a gruesome imagination,' Elizabeth complained, following her down the narrow steps into the courtyard.

'Even Cesare Borgia was here,' Vicky said. 'I wonder if he poisoned anyone on his trip. We might find a few skeletons in the secret passages.'

'We might leave one, too,' said Elizabeth, grinning at Aunt Fleur. 'Shall we lock her up and run?'

Vicky ignored her. 'Not to mention Cardinal Richelieu, he owned this place later.'

'I should think he was good for a skeleton or two,' Elizabeth agreed.

The afternoon sun was still blindingly hot, but inside the caves beneath the Donjon du Coudray she felt suddenly cold; the darkness and damp walls were oppressive. Vicky and Aunt Fleur walked slowly with the guide, listening to him, and Elizabeth felt like going back to the entrance. She hated the claustrophobic atmosphere pressing down on her, she felt smothered, unable to breathe.

The hair clung to the back of her neck, and she pushed it away with a shaky hand, pausing. The others walked on and she was about to catch up with them when she heard a faint sound, breathing, rustling—she wasn't sure what it was, but it came from the darkness beyond her. The voices of her aunt and her sister faded, she heard a whispering. 'Never let you go, never, never . . .'

She had her eyes shut, she didn't dare to open

them. Something cold touched her face and she screamed, her lids flying back to be dazzled by sunlight. Totally disorientated, she stared into it with wild incredulity and then saw Aunt Fleur looking down at her, face pale and worried.

'How do you feel, dear?'

Elizabeth looked at her blankly. Vicky's face hovered beside Aunt Fleur, a frown pulling her brows together. 'What . . ' Elizabeth whispered.

'You fainted,' Vicky told her. 'In the passages—don't you remember?'

'If I'd realised you suffered from claustrophobia I'd never have taken you down there,' Aunt Fleur said.

'We thought you were with us,' Vicky explained. 'Then we heard a crash and looked round and there you were on the floor, out cold. You gave us a shock, I can tell you!'

'How did I get out here?' Elizabeth asked, sitting up, her head still slightly dizzy.

'The guide carried you—poor man, he was afraid you'd die on him. He's getting a doctor.'

There was an interested little crowd watching them, Elizabeth flushed as she realised that she was the centre of so much attention. 'I'm fine now,' she said. 'I feel a real idiot, though. I don't need a doctor, I just want to get home.'

'I think you ought to see the doctor,' Aunt Fleur said firmly. 'I'm sure it was probably just claustrophobia, but it's best to be on the safe side.'

By the time Elizabeth had had a brief examination by the local doctor who drove up five minutes later, it was closing time. They

walked back slowly to the car and Elizabeth slid
into the back seat with a sigh of relief. When they
got back to Aunt Fleur's house she allowed
herself to be pushed upstairs to bed and fell
asleep almost at once, the shutters closed and the
room full of late afternoon shadows, blue and
purple which slowly changed to rose-gold, as the
sun finally set for the night. Outside the trees
were whispering, there was a constant sound of
birds and the distant running of the river,
tranquil noises which made a soft lullaby,
calming her unstrung nerves.

When she woke up again it was very hot in the
room, she felt airless. The moon was up, leaving
thin spears of silver light across the walls.
Elizabeth got out of bed and went over to the
window to open the shutters, but it made little
difference, the air was heavy and humid, as
though a storm might be going to break, but
there were no clouds in the night sky. She leaned
on the sill, snatching breath. Was it almost dawn?
She felt as if she had slept for hours, she was
wide awake and she knew she would never get
back to sleep.

She dressed in jeans and a T-shirt and quietly
crept down the stairs to the kitchen, made herself
some coffee and ate a slice of crisp-crusted bread
with it, spread with Aunt Fleur's thick, home-
made cherry jam. There were several cherry trees
in the garden, and Aunt Fleur bottled and
preserved the dark red fruit.

It was almost five oclock and the sky showed
some light, although in this thickly wooded river
valley the sun rose late over the horizon. There

was no sign of anyone else stirring, so Elizabeth went out, too active to stay indoors any longer.

Taking the bridle path through the woods, she walked down towards the river, her feet grating on the sandy track, her way lit only by faint glimmerings of light from the sky. The trees breathed all around her, a rabbit scampered into the ferns as she came into sight, its white scut vanished so fast she only just saw it, birds flew quickly from one side of the path to the other, calling. She was not the only inhabitant of the dawn. At this time of day it was usually cooler, but today the sky seemed to press down on the back of her head, her shirt was already sticking to her and her hair was damply clustered on her nape.

She emerged on the river bank among the trees. The water ran slowly there, the surface gleaming dark, a moving mirror to the sky and trees. Elizabeth walked for a while, then sat down on the dew-damp grass, her knees up, her chin on them, staring at the river, listening to it as it whirled and whispered over the stones.

She was tempted to strip off and take a swim, she was so hot. Standing up, she peered along the banks on either side. There were no houses down here, she saw nobody moving in the half-light. She told herself it was a ridiculous idea, but it was so beautiful; the silence broken only by muffled sounds of birds and barely stirred leaves, by the gently running river and the grass under her feet.

Impulsively she pulled down her jeans, stripped off her T-shirt and, in bra and panties, ran down to the water. She took another quick look around, then took off her underclothes and left them in a neat pile on the grass before slipping into the water. A little shudder of pleasure went through her as her hot skin felt the coolness envelop it. She swam slowly into the centre of the river, hoping the weed was not too thick there.

It was magical, sliding like a pale fish through the dark water, her hair trailing like water weed behind her. She floated on her back for a while, letting the river ripple along her body, watching the sky beginning to colour with rosy fire behind the black outlines of the trees, the flame spread softly, washed the whole horizon and began to fade into a pinky gold. Reluctantly, she turned to swim back to the bank and waded out, beginning to shiver. Her hair dripped down her back and she reached up to wring it free of water, then froze in shock as a figure stepped out from the woods, a blacker shape detaching itself from darkness as she looked at it in consternation.

She was so shaken that it was a minute before she moved, she stood in horrified stillness, her body arched; arms lifted, her wet breasts high and rounded in a stretched movement, her flesh gleaming in the dawn light. Then she darted at her clothes, picked them up and with trembling fingers began to dress. She heard the footsteps coming closer and didn't look towards the approaching figure. Her clothes clung to her wet body, she was sick with relief as she zipped up her jeans, and could face him. She had not seen his face, but she knew it was Yves de Lavalle.

'I know,' she stammered before he could speak,

'I'm trespassing again. I'm sorry, I'll try to stay off your land.' Looking up at him, she read no expression on his face, but the dark eyes were colder than the water from which she had just come: colder and deeper. Looking into them she felt afraid.

'It is dangerous to swim in the river, especially alone. If you got into difficulties, nobody would hear you. This is a very isolated spot.' What he said was very sensible, but somehow his icy voice made the words menacing, there seemed far more behind the remarks than mere practical common sense—but perhaps she was letting her imagination run riot again.

He stood barring her path, she had to walk past him to get back into the woods and home. 'It was just an impulse,' she said huskily. 'I couldn't sleep . . .'

'Guilty conscience?' he asked, the words tipped with flint.

She faced him out, hiding the flinch the question caused. 'It was so hot,' she evaded.

'You can see his tower from here,' Yves de Lavalle said, and Elizabeth stiffened. She did not look round, she took a step to walk past the man blocking her way, and he closed an iron hand around her arm, twisting her round to face the river again. 'There,' he said, pointing. She had refused to look at it, but now she had no choice.

The old stone tower rose among the trees farther along the bank, she saw a wood pigeon flap from the crumbling walls and wing away.

'It's empty now,' Yves de Lavalle told her.

'The local people say it's haunted, they won't go near it after sunset.'

Elizabeth swallowed, shivering. 'I don't believe in ghosts.' It was the truth, she never had, but what was happening to her now—was it her own mind playing tricks on her, or was Damian's obsessive love still reaching out to her from the darkness? Could thoughts and feelings linger after death, could they flutter in the air like moths in starlight?

'Don't you?' Yves de Lavalle asked her with icy derision. He put out a long finger and touched the side of her cheek. 'Your face is wet.'

'I've just been swimming!' She shivered again, looking away from the tower. 'And I'm cold—let go, please, I want to get home and dry myself.'

'Cold?' he repeated and smiled with a dry twist of the lips. 'Yes,' he said. 'You *are* cold.' Again that echo of other meanings, and Elizabeth wrenched her arm free, very much afraid of him.

His hand shot out before she could walk away and enclosed her face. His mouth touched hers. It was icy, but the ice burned, she gasped in shock at the touch of it. For a moment he inflicted the kiss on her shaking lips, then he moved back. 'Yes, you are cold,' he said again, and Elizabeth ran from him, her body trembling so violently that she almost fell.

CHAPTER FIVE

THAT morning they drove over to the nearest market town to do some shopping. Aunt Fleur and Elizabeth left Vicky in the charcuterie greedily inspecting a delicious array of cold cooked meats and ready-to-eat salads of all kinds from diced beetroot to fine strands of carrot coated in dressing, while they went to the boulangerie and bought freshly baked bread.

'And some pain-au-chocolat,' said Elizabeth, looking at the flaky pastry rolls which had chocolate hidden inside them. 'Vicky loves them, even if they are meant for children.'

'She looked about six this morning with her hair in bunches and her face all pink from sleep,' Aunt Fleur said, laughing. 'You were up early, weren't you?'

'Yes,' Elizabeth said flatly, then changed the subject before her aunt could say anything else. 'You haven't forgotten that Teddy Hertford is coming to lunch, have you?'

'Of course I hadn't forgotten—I thought we'd have a picnic lunch in the woods if it's fine. I want to show him several herbs that only grow there.' She paid the baker and said: '*Au revoir, m'sieur,*' then added: '*Au revoir, mesdames,*' to the other customers as she and Elizabeth left the shop. A chorus answered them. When Elizabeth first visited France she hadn't realised how

careful the French were about such formal
courtesies. Cheerfully casual herself, she had
been taken aback to be stared at in shops and
shown no answering warmth. 'They're not very
friendly,' she had said to Damian, who laughed
and said: 'Let me explain the French to you, my
darling . . .'

'I wish you would,' she had groaned.

'When you go into a shop you must say good
morning to everyone in there, and when you
leave you say goodbye. You mustn't just ignore
them, they'll think you're rude and badly brought
up.' He had given her a sudden, vivid, amused
smile. 'It may seem very formal, but it keeps life
on a human footing—in France even buying a
cabbage is treated as an important event. Good
manners are very important here, they show
respect for other people.'

Damian was English, but he had lived in
France for most of his life; he thought like a
Frenchman, he admired French culture and
attitudes, perhaps because his own nature was so
deeply emotional that he felt he needed that
formal framework; it helped him to contain and
control feelings which might otherwise have
ripped him apart.

'Penny for your thoughts,' said Aunt Fleur,
laughing, and Elizabeth started, brought back
suddenly to the narrow medieval street; the sunlit
square beyond, where some old men played
boules, the little silvery balls clicking as they
touched. That was a ritual, too; unhurried,
thoughtful, but fought out fiercely, nevertheless,
defeat or victory mattered for all the formality

with which the old men played.

'I was thinking how French things are here,' Elizabeth said incoherently, and Aunt Fleur laughed again, her face very amused.

'All the better, don't you think? The world outside gets smaller every day, cities look identical whether you go east or west; skyscrapers and motorways, hamburgers and Coca-Cola—sometimes you wonder if we'll all end up as robots, but at least in France they try to keep their own identity. All this fast food—how can anyone enjoy it? It tastes like plastic, it looks like plastic. This is a plastic world. No, give me food that someone has spent time and trouble getting ready, food that tastes of what's in it, food that's beautiful to look at and even better to eat.'

'Everything has to be instant today,' said Elizabeth, her eyes teasing. 'People want to save time, they don't want to create works of art to eat, they just sling a frozen dinner into the oven or open a tin.'

Aunt Fleur shuddered. 'What do they save all this time for? What do they do with it when they've saved it?'

'Watch TV,' said Elizabeth, laughing.

'What a way to live! No wonder they look irritated, their stomach linings are being eaten away.' She went into the pork butcher's shop and Elizabeth waved to Vicky, who was standing under the plane trees idly watching the old men play *boules*. Vicky sauntered over and a boy on a bicycle swerved, staring at her curvaceous figure in the tight red jeans and white T-shirt. She grinned at him and he went red but grinned back, then bounced off on the cobbles, his machine rattling.

'Stop flirting with strangers,' Elizabeth scolded with amusement. 'He nearly fell off, poor boy!'

'That will teach him to keep his eyes on the road,' said Vicky with satisfaction. 'I got some grapes and plums and all the salad stuff Aunt Fleur wanted. Anything else?'

'I think we've finished our shopping.'

Aunt Fleur came out of the butcher's shop and Elizabeth took her heavy basket. 'Let's have some coffee,' she suggested. There was a small bar across the square which had a few tables out on the pavement. They walked across there and sat down. The sunshine was brilliant, but somewhere a coming storm rumbled and the air was humid, sticky. They had no sooner finished their coffee than a cloud covered the sun, the sky turned dark and they had to run back to the car before the first heavy drops of rain began to hit the pavements.

Vicky looked out of the car gloomily as they drove through streets running with rain. 'Teddy won't come now, I don't suppose. No point, really, we wouldn't be able to go looking for his cherished flora.'

'It may clear,' said Aunt Fleur, cocking an eye at the stormy sky.

'Some hope.' Vicky sighed deeply, and Elizabeth laughed.

'Don't be such a pessimist!'

They had to run for it when they got back to the house, their arms full of bags of food. Before

Elizabeth had got into the little hall her blonde
hair had been saturated, it clung to her scalp in
dark strands, her face was wet and her blue shirt
stuck to her back. When she had dumped what
she carried in the kitchen, she ran upstairs to
change into dry clothes. It was the second time
that day that she had had to change—the jeans
and shirt she had been wearing when she went
down to the river at dawn had been damp and
plastered with mud when she got back. Luckily,
neither Vicky nor their aunt had been up when
Elizabeth got back, so she had been able to slip
into her room and change without being seen.
She was going to have to do some washing soon
or she would run out of clean clothes.

She put on a pleated navy-blue and white dress
and brushed her hair dry, leaving it gleaming,
loose, around her face, then went over to the
window to glance out at the garden. The sky was
a leaden colour, the trees lashed to and fro in the
wind, water ran in the gutters and splashed in the
deep puddles which had formed on the paths.
Beyond Aunt Fleur's garden lay the dark woods,
a mist of rain over them. Elizabeth was cold, she
shivered, and remembered the icy touch of Yves
de Lavalle's mouth—why had he kissed her like
that? At the time she had seen it as a calculated
insult. He had kissed her out of contempt, with
hostility, but now she felt again the strangely
erotic heat which she had sensed behind his cold
kiss, and a tremor of recoil ran through her.

He was married to a girl who obviously loved
him passionately—why had he kissed her at all?
What motive had he had? To make sure she knew

how much he despised her? He had said very
little, but every word had stabbed, been carefully
chosen, icy—yet how thin was the ice?

Elizabeth had the feeling that it was a very thin
crust, and that dark waters lay beneath. Onc false
step and you might find yourself plunging into
fathomless depths—she shuddered at the idea of
what secrets his cold mask hid.

He had been Damian's friend—how much had
he heard about her, what had Damian told him?
It was embarrasing to think that a stranger might
have heard some warped version of what had
happened between herself and Damian. She
could easily imagine how Damian would have
described her; he wouldn't have been flattering,
his jealousy had made him bitter.

Even if she dared try to talk to Yves de
Lavalle about it, he wouldn't believe her—he
would believe Damian because Damian was
dead and Yves de Lavalle had been with him in
that car, but he was still alive, and Elizabeth
suspected that part of his hostility to her came
from a sense of guilt buried inside himself.
Guilty conscience? he had sneered at her this
morning, and she had flinched because he was
right, of course, but now that she thought about
it calmly she could see that his accusation had
been as much directed at himself. They were
both alive—Damian was dead, and death has a
terrible power over the living.

Teddy Hertford arrived punctually at one
o'clock—it had stopped raining, but the sky was
still dull, clouds sagged over the woods and the
air was clammy.

'I brought my wellies!' he told Vicky as she let him in, and Vicky made a wry face.

'You're going to need them—the paths in the wood have turned into swamps.'

'A little thing like rain doesn't bother me,' Teddy said happily, and Vicky looked at him with a sarcastic smile.

'Nice to be obsessed, is it?'

'You should try it some time, at least life's never dull,' Teddy retorted.

'Children, children!' Aunt Fleur intervened, laughing. 'Come and have lunch before you start throwing things at each other.'

Teddy looked at the hors d'oeuvres laid out on the table, his face eager. 'Delicious! I'm really looking forward to some home cooking—I'm living on bread and cheese in my tent. I can't cook.'

'Can't cook?' Vicky asked, raising her brows.

Elizabeth started to laugh. 'Vicky only goes out with men who can cook,' she said, then stopped talking, her mouth open, as her sister gave her a dagger-sharp glare of affront and fury.

Teddy gave Vicky a bland smile, his eyes innocent. 'Going to proposition me, were you? I'd better borrow a cookery book fast, hadn't I?'

'Funny!' Vicky bit out, very pink. She gave Elizabeth another bitter look. 'My sister jumps to conclusions,' she said viciously. 'Wrong conclusions,' she added.

'Well, that's a relief,' said Teddy, helping himself to an anchovy. 'I'm old-fashioned, as it happens—I do my own propositioning.'

Vicky seethed visibly and Elizabeth felt

uncomfortable. 'It was just a joke,' she said, and Vicky muttered: 'Ha, ha . . .'

After lunch they all set off into the woods, tramping under the dripping trees, talking. The sky was turning blue, but the wind still whipped through the branches, howling like an animal in pain, and Elizabeth was cold, she could not summon up any wild enthusiasm for plants. She had been half inclined to stay in the house, but that would have meant that she was alone with her thoughts, and that idea didn't make her too happy, either.

She fell behind as the others plunged in among ferns and rooted under bushes, wandering along with her hands in her pockets and wishing she was somewhere else. Suddenly she found herself alone on the river bank. Heaven alone knew where the others had got to—she heard their excited voices at a distance. Elizabeth looked absently along the grey-green river, the surface littered with debris from the storm: leaves, broken branches, an old car tyre and a stiff, drowned rat. She averted her gaze from the dead rat and found herself staring at Damian's tower.

It was very old, built of stone and flint which the rain had darkened, so that it had a slate-blue gleam in the faint sunlight. Elizabeth walked towards it slowly, then froze as she saw that the door was swinging open in the wind.

Was someone living there? Damian had never talked much about his background, he showed no interest in his family and avoided Elizabeth's questions about them. It hadn't occurred to her until now that someone must have inherited his estate. All he owned, so far as she knew, was the tower where he had lived for years, but his paintings must be valuable, if any had been found unsold at his death.

She stood watching the open door, listening for sounds of movements. There were none. After a few minutes she warily went over to the open door. 'Hallo?' she called up the winding stone steps which led to the living quarters on the first floor. Damian had used the base of the tower for storage. The place had been in use for centuries, but the usage had altered from time to time. Once it had been a watermill, another time it had been a net-house, during the period when the river was full of fish and fishing was a local industry, and during the eighteenth century it had been used to store guns and gun powder, which had exploded one night and blown a great hole in the walls. Damian had used it as a home and a studio, enlarging the windows on the first floor to give more light.

Nobody answered her. She called again in French—the same silence. After a long hesitation she went inside and stole quietly up the stairs. She couldn't resist the temptation to see Damian's home again.

There was a faintly musty dampness about the tower, the walls were clammy and retained the rain longer than brick, and there was no damp course. The tower was built of massive, irregular stones quarried locally. An old rope formed the hand-hold on the stairs, it was slung through iron hoops nailed into the stone walls. The sound of her footsteps echoed slightly, she heard herself breathing in nervous rapidity. At the top of the stairs another door stood open.

'Hallo, anybody there?' Elizabeth asked too loudly, and her voice rang in the tower with that empty sound buildings can give off when nobody has lived there for a long time.

She pushed the door wider. It creaked and she jumped. Then something moved and a little scream rasped in her throat. She looked, eyes wide, and saw a long tail disappear, thin and snaky. Elizabeth closed her eyes, shuddering. A rat! Damian had often complained about them, they came in from the river bank and ate his bread. He used to put down traps for them, he wouldn't use rat poison in case it killed one of the cats from the nearby farms. Damian had loved cats, he painted them in idle moments and loved to sketch them; his sketchbooks had been full of little drawings of cats.

She looked around the room, it was bitterly familiar, unchanged since she last saw it. Circular, with windows on all sides, the walls were painted white and hung with sketches, oils, watercolours, all done by Damian or his friends. The floor was uncarpeted, the wood highly polished and stained a deep dark brown. Some old, balloon-backed chairs stood against one wall, their upholstery a wine-coloured plush, there was a table, a desk covered in papers, a small couch and a tiny occasional table on which stood a green silk lamp. Damian did not enjoy luxury, he had bought most of his furniture second-hand and had renovated it himself; he was very good with his hands.

Elizabeth walked around the room, looking at objects in a dazed, dull passivity. They were things, shells left behind by a man who had never rated possessions very highly, he had touched them, held them, but they were empty, they held nothing of him now.

Among the papers on his desk she saw a sketchbook lying open. She looked at it and then did a double-take as she recognised herself.

Her hands trembled as she picked up the large pad. Damian had drawn her coming out of the river, naked, her hair hanging limply around her face, her arms up to catch it. Elizabeth's throat was dry. She was in shock as she looked at the economically sketched line of her uplifted breasts, at the curved flank and the damp little triangle of hair between her thighs.

When had he drawn it?

Her gaze moved to the page facing that one and she saw other sketches of herself: in jeans with a shirt on, walking, her hair blown round her face, turning her head to look over her shoulder, staring straight out of the page with wide-open eyes.

Grief made her eyes sting, she had to bite her lips to keep back the tears. The little drawings had such life, such immediacy, they could have been drawn yesterday, but the hand which had had such brilliant skill would never draw again.

She leaned against the cold stone wall, her eyes closed, fighting with her tears. When she felt calmer she put the sketchbook down and was about to move away when her eye flicked over the drawing, and something odd struck her. She picked it up again, studying it, not sure if she was imagining things.

She couldn't quite place her sense of something wrong at first, she kept looking from drawing to drawing intently, frowning.

It was her hair, she realised—in one sketch it blew around her face, loose, the ends of it out of sight behind her shoulders. In the next it hung softly down over her shoulders, framing her face.

In both it was far too long. Her hair was that length now, she had let it grow without having it trimmed while she was in New York, but why had Damian drawn it that long two years ago, when she had had short hair?

Stiffening, she looked at the drawing of herself coming up out of the river. The hair was wet in that sketch, but it was still too long.

She turned the other pages, looking for further sketches of herself, but found none—the others were all of natural objects; trees, the river, the tower, a cat.

Looking back at the drawings of herself, she carefully compared the style in them with the style Damian had used two years ago. There were no visible differences that she could see—all the sketches had been done swiftly, using few lines, capturing an expression, an impression, as economically as possible. She was no art expert, but she had spent hours watching Damian draw and she was certain that the sketches were his—unless some equally clever artist was deliberately copying his style.

But why on earth should anyone do that? Putting the pad down, she walked around the walls and stared at the other sketches and paintings hanging there.

Damian's work was worth quite a lot of money now, of course. It might be worth somebody's while to fake a few paintings, but if anyone was good enough to do that surely they would choose to imitate somebody far more famous than Damian?

She walked back to the sketchbook and looked again, with a suddenly hot face, at the drawing of herself in the nude coming out of the river. If Damian hadn't done that, who could have done? Who had seen her swimming that morning?

A sound made her spin, her hands shaking so much that she dropped the book and it fell to the floor, the pages fluttering.

Yves de Lavalle leaned in the doorway, staring at her with narrowed hostile eyes. 'What are you doing in here? Do you make a habit of trespassing?' he demanded coldly.

Elizabeth was too staggered to say anything for a moment, her heart beating hard against her ribs, then she stammered: 'Do you own this, too?' Had he bought the tower after Damian's death?

'You don't,' he retorted. 'You have no right to be in here.'

'The door was open . . . I wondered . . .'

'What?' he asked, strolling into the room in a slow way which alarmed her all over again. She felt as though he was stalking up on her, his body had a feral grace, it reminded her of a cat which has been domesticated but has gone wild, its movements all threat but with a dangerous intelligence in its eyes. When she just stared at him, he said again: 'What did you wonder? If it had all been a mistake? If Damian was alive in here, working at his easel?'

She stared, white to her hairline.

'I've often come here and been sure I'd find him,' he said, but he was not being sympathetic or reassuring, his voice had the hiss of cold steel and his eyes were those of an enemy. 'Every time I see this tower I get that feeling—this is his place, it belongs to him.' He was so close now that their bodies almost touched, yet he held himself apart from her, mentally and physically, his mouth had a contemptuous twist to it as he looked down at her. 'And he wouldn't want you here.' His tone made Elizabeth wince and she was suddenly angry.

'You've no right to say that, how do you know?' How could anyone but herself and Damian know the truth about how they felt? What made this man think he could see inside their heads?

'Are you feeling guilty?' Yves de Lavalle asked her in icy mockery, and she looked at him, trembling.

'Are you?'

He stared back, his brows pulling together, that smooth, pale face otherwise expressionless. There wasn't a line on it, sometimes when she saw it she instinctively shuddered at the masklike coldness of it. In a way it was beautiful, with a powerful male beauty which was charged with menace, but a menace she could never quite pin down, it smouldered somewhere behind those deep black eyes but if she stared into them, trying

Love, romance, intrigue...all are captured for you by Mills & Boon's top-selling authors.

TAKE FOUR EXCITING BOOKS ABSOLUTELY FREE

Four exciting Mills & Boon Romances have been specially selected for you to enjoy FREE and without any obligation. You'll fall in love with the fascinating characters, the intrigue and the exotic locations of these marvellous stories. Each romance will hold you spellbound from the first page to the last loving embrace. To find out how you can claim your FOUR FREE BOOKS, please turn over.

See overleaf for super offer.

Do not affix postage stamps if posted in Gt. Britain, Channel Islands or N. Ireland.

BR LICENCE NO. CN81

Mills & Boon Reader Service, PO Box 236, CROYDON, Surrey CR9 9EL.

2

Mills & Boon, the world's most popular publisher of romantic fiction, invites you to take these four books free.

FOUR BOOKS FREE

As a special introductory offer to the Mills & Boon Reader Service, we will send you four superb Mills & Boon Romances ABSOLUTELY FREE and WITHOUT OBLIGATION.

Become a subscriber, and you will receive each month:

THE NEWEST ROMANCES – reserved at the printers and delivered direct to you by Mills & Boon.

POSTAGE AND PACKING FREE – you only pay the same as you would in the shops.

NO COMMITMENT – you receive books only for as long as you want.

FREE MONTHLY NEWSLETTER – keeps you up-to-date with new books and book bargains.

HELPFUL, FRIENDLY SERVICE from the girls at Mills & Boon. You can ring us any time on 01-684 2141.

THE FOUR FREE BOOKS SHOWN HERE ARE OUR SPECIAL GIFT TO YOU.
THEY ARE YOURS TO KEEP REGARDLESS OF WHETHER YOU
WISH TO BUY FURTHER BOOKS.

Just fill in and post the coupon today.

🂠 Mills & Boon

Mills & Boon Reader Service,
PO Box 236, Croydon,
Surrey CR9 3RU.

NO
STAMP
NEEDED

✂ - - - - - - - - - - - - - - - - - - -

FREE BOOKS CERTIFICATE

To: Mills & Boon Reader Service, PO Box 236, Croydon, Surrey CR9 9EL.

Please send me, free and without obligation the four Mills & Boon Romances illustrated in this leaflet, and reserve a Reader Service Subscription for me. If I decide to subscribe I shall, from the beginning of the month following my free parcel of books, receive six new books each month for £5.70 post and packing free. If I decide not to subscribe, I shall write to you within 14 days. The free books are mine to keep in any case.

I understand that I may cancel my subscription at any time simply by writing to you. I am over 18 years of age.

Please write in BLOCK CAPITALS

Name_____

Address_____

_____

_____ Post Code_____

SEND NO MONEY – TAKE NO RISKS.   **10R 36**

One offer per household. Offer applies in UK only – overseas send for details. If price changes are necessary you will be notified

to decipher their message, she found herself going almost dizzy, losing track of her own thoughts.

'I wasn't driving that car,' he said shortly. 'He was.' He gave a short sight, stifled at birth. 'That's why he died—he was pinned behind the driver's wheel . . .'

'Don't!' she burst out, turning away and trembling violently at the image.

He caught her arms and wrenched her round again, making her face him, bending down towards her to speak very softly, each word icy. 'We were talking about you the day we crashed. Chantal reminded me yesterday—he had had lunch with us, and had talked about nothing else. Maybe that's why we crashed. He was in a wild mood because of you.' He frowned, his face darkly restless, and Elizabeth pulled free, taking a step backward. Her foot skidded on the sketch-book. Yves glanced down, then bent and picked the book up, staring at the drawing of her coming out of the river. Elizabeth tried to take the book from him and he looked up at her, one brow raised.

'Why the blush? I've seen you naked before.' He let his eyes flick down over her contemptuously. 'You've got a lovely body, I'm sure others have told you so. Don't pretend to be shy, it doesn't impress me.'

'I wasn't pretending anything!' she muttered, the hair on the back of her neck prickling at the way he was staring at her.

'You could drive some men mad,' Yves said, watching her. 'You drove Damian out of his mind with your affairs, didn't you?'

'No! That's not true . . .'

'Isn't it?' His terse retort called her a liar, his twisted smile insulted her. 'You got bored, you flirted with other men and when Damian got angry you walked out on him. I know all about it—don't lie to me.'

'You don't understand,' Elizabeth stammered. 'Damian was so intense . . .'

He laughed harshly. 'And intensity bores you? You prefer to have fun, don't you? You wanted to have a good time, enjoy life—you can't take real emotion, it embarrasses you.'

'Stop putting words into my mouth! That isn't how it was . . .'

He took a step closer, the fathomless black eyes glittering inches away from her own. 'How was it, then? What *did* you want?' His hands closed over her shoulders and he smiled down at her mockingly. 'Let's see if I can guess . . .'

His mouth touched hers, for a second she flinched from the icy contact, then the ice dissolved and flame leapt up between them; he forced her lips to part, a hungry wildness in the pressure, probing her mouth with consuming intensity, and now his hands held her face, forcing her head back so that she could not escape the demand of his kiss. Elizabeth instinctively clutched at him to save herself from falling, her hands clamped in his shirt. He put one arm round her and pulled her against him, and her hands shook as they moved upwards and clung round his neck. She felt his hand move exploringly, it touched her breast, and she groaned with closed eyes, limp and yielding. His other hand ran down her back, following the indentation of her spine, her zip softly peeled open and he slid his hand inside, caressing her naked back.

The contact, skin on skin, had a sensual impact which blocked out all her attempts to think, her mind was too busy receiving clamorous messages from her body to be able to cope with the reasons why she shouldn't let him do this to her. Her dress slid away, she didn't even know it, her hands clasping his head, her mouth clinging to his as though it would kill her to end the deep, heated kisses. She hadn't kissed anyone like this, or been kissed, for two years. A long-denied hunger was driving her, she needed to touch him, unaware at that moment who he was, only knowing that her hands craved the feel of the close, male body.

Her fingers were trembling, she was ice-cold and feverish at the same time, opening his shirt, stroking his throat, his shoulders, her touch moving from the muscled strength of his neck to the warm, firm chest, the dark hairs running in a wedge from the midriff upwards clinging to her perspiring palms as she touched him.

He nudged her backwards with his knee and she fell down against the couch, her eyes flying open in shock, her mind surfacing again from the hypnotic eroticism of their lovemaking, to realise that she was totally naked, he had stripped her as he kissed her. She gasped, looked up at him, face burning, and Yves de Lavalle stood their watching her, a savage smile twisting his mouth as he slowly did up his shirt.

'That was what you wanted, wasn't it?' he asked, the words tipped with ice. 'Five minutes and I could have had you—any man could have you, you're a lady who falls on her back for anyone.'

Elizabeth wished she was dead, she hated herself, she hated him, and in those cruel black eyes she had no difficulty reading an answering hatred—he made no effort to hide his contempt and distaste. Humiliated, she looked away, and at that moment heard Vicky calling her.

'Liz? Liz, where the hell have you got to? Liz?'

Yves de Lavalle turned his head, listening. He walked to the door without haste. 'Get dressed, get out of here and stay off my land,' he said coldly, and then he was gone, she heard his footsteps on the stone steps going down.

CHAPTER SIX

'You haven't forgotten that we're going to Angers today with Teddy, have you?' Vicky asked her three days later. They were having breakfast in a kitchen flooded with sunlight, Elizabeth was watching the lace-like shadows of the trees moving on the floor and she started as her sister spoke to her, looking up.

'What?'

'Miles away,' said Vicky, making a face. 'Wake up, Liz! I said, we're going to Angers today.'

Frowning, Elizabeth said: 'Would you mind if I don't come? Yesterday was a heavy day, I'm worn out with all this sightseeing.' They had spent the day at Chenonceau, the most popular of the châteaux on the Loire; tramping around the elegant apartments in which first Diane de Poitiers and then Catherine de Medici had lived, and afterwards walking through the green park for a while before they hired a rowing boat and amused themselves by looping their way in and out of the narrow arches of the bridge on which the château was built. Vicky had been quite keen at first, but had soon complained that her arm muscles ached, and Elizabeth had ended up doing most of the work.

'You poor thing,' Vicky said, gaily mocking. 'Too much for you, was it? All that rowing?

You're out of condition, that's your problem.'

'My problem,' Elizabeth retorted, 'is my sister; who insists on hiring rowing boats and then makes me do the rowing!'

Aunt Fleur had been watching her with a thoughtful expression and now she said: 'If you really want to stay at home, I'll stay too, dear. You don't want to be alone all day.'

Vicky looked alarmed, biting her lip. Elizabeth was tempted to laugh at her expression—her sisters did not want to be alone with Teddy, whenever the two of them were alone there was a heavy atmosphere, and Elizabeth had noticed that Vicky always made sure she wasn't left alone with him.

'Don't be silly, I'll be fine—I'll have a quiet, lazy day in the garden; read a book, listen to some records, get down to the letters I still haven't written yet. Mum and Dad will be dying to know about our holiday.'

Aunt Fleur hesitated, her eyes uncertain.

'I mean it,' Elizabeth said firmly.

'She's a big girl now,' Vicky said in relief. 'Come on, Aunt Fleur, you aren't ready yet, Teddy will be here any minute . . . I'm dying to see the deer at Angers, I saw them on a postcard of the Château. It's a super idea, to keep deer in the old moat. Can you feed them?'

'Certainly not,' Aunt Fleur told her. 'You aren't allowed into the moat at all, you only see them from the drawbridge and the walls . . .'

Their voices died away as they went out. Elizabeth carried a deckchair out into the garden and placed it under a tree, collected up some paperback books and her sunglasses, went upstairs to change into a pair of white shorts and a brief top which tied across her midriff in a large red bow. Teddy drove up and she waved from the door as the others left for Angers, smiling as brightly as she could in an effort to seem normal. That was how it had been for the past three days, ever since she saw Yves de Lavalle in the tower—she had had a bright, phoney smile glued to her face from the minute she got up to the minute she went to bed, and she was sick of it.

She had barely had time to huddle herself back into her clothes that day when she heard Vicky's voice at the door of the tower; it had sounded high, nervous, uneasy. 'Liz? Are you in there?'

She had run shaking hands over her tousled hair and gone down, hoping that no glimpse of what had just happened would show in her face, hoping that Yves would have vanished. She could not have borne to see him again, to face him with her sister and Aunt Fleur watching, to see the savage mockery in those black eyes of his, because she knew she couldn't give the appearance of calm while he was looking at her. But he had gone, she had been able to pretend a casual smile and say: 'Found any good plants?'

'What on earth were you doing in there?' Vicky had asked, going straight to the point in her usual charming fashion.

'The door was open, I just went in,' Elizabeth had explained, and smiled at Teddy because he seemed the safest person to be looking at. He would have no idea why her aunt and sister were looking at her in that worried way, he was standing with his hands in his pockets staring curiously up at the tower.

'What is this place?' he had asked.

Vicky hadn't been listening to him. 'Is anyone living there now?' she was asking Aunt Fleur, who shook her head.

'No. I can't think why the door was open, it should be locked.'

'It looks medieval,' Teddy had pronounced.

'It is,' Aunt Fleur told him. 'Older than the Château by four centuries.'

'Does it belong to the same people?' asked Teddy, and Aunt Fleur half glanced at Elizabeth and hesitated before she agreed.

'Yes.'

'Does it?' asked Vicky, looking taken aback. 'Well, well!'

Elizabeth had walked away, her stomach knotted with agonising cramp. She had needed desperately to be alone, but she hadn't had a chance since then except at night in her own room, and then she had been too tired to think, she had fallen into a sleep too deep to be restful, waking each morning with her jaw aching with tension. It had been exhausting to keep up that falsely cheerful expression hour after hour. She marvelled that neither of the other two had noticed how unreal her smile was—to her it seemed blindingly obvious, her facial muscles seemed to be locked in rigor mortis, at times.

In the garden she stretched out on the deckchair, her sunglasses dropped on to her book, and let the sunlight pour down over her.

She had already caught the sun to some extent,
her tan was much deeper on arms and legs and
face. It was not yet too hot, later she must put
some oil on her skin, but just for half an hour she
would lie here and let the silence seep into her
bones.

Whenever she remembered those moments in
Yves de Lavalle's arms she felt sick; her stomach
heaved in painful self-disgust. How could she
have let him do that to her? She didn't know the
man, she didn't like him, he frightened her—
what madness had made her go crazy like that,
tempted her to lose all control, self-respect and
decency, as if she secretly wanted to act like the
sort of woman he had accused her of being?

Her mind seethed with questions, like the earth
under a stone, crawling with secret life. She kept
her eyes shut as though that might shut the door
on those questions—but of course it didn't. She
had to know—why?

She had condemned herself. He had called her
an amoral bitch and she had gone ahead and
behaved like one, and she couldn't even understand it herself, she didn't recognise herself in the
woman who had touched a stranger, pulsating
with desire, and let him make love to her without
a single protest. There might be a shred of an
excuse for her if she had fallen in love with him,
but Yves de Lavalle scared her stiff. Whenever
she saw him the back of her neck went cold, she
recoiled from him in alarm. He was hardly a
charming man and although he had a striking face
there was something about it that made her
shrink. She had no idea what he was like behind

that cold, handsome face, it was too much of a mask, too controlled and aware of itself.

Her lids lifted and her bewildered, disturbed eyes stared up at the blue sky, remembering the drawings she had seen in that sketchbook. They could have been drawn by Damian—in any other context she would have sworn he had done them, they were so much in his style. Yet how could he have done them? Why would he have drawn her with long hair, when she had always had short hair when he knew here?

Someone had been carefully imitating his techniques—who? Yves de Lavalle? But why should he? According to Aunt Fleur he was a very wealthy man, a banker from Paris who could easily afford to buy an old château and have it expensively renovated. Why would he want to imitate Damian's drawings?

Her skin was hot and tight from the sun. She sat up and picked up the bottle of suntan oil, unscrewed it and poured some of the contents into her palm, slowly rubbing it into her arms and legs.

There was one reason why Yves de Lavalle might be faking Damian's work, one reason why he might have deliberately set out to humiliate her the other day—but it was so warped and extraordinary that Elizabeth flinched away from believing it could be true.

He might not have been driving the car when it crashed, but she had a strong suspicion that Yves felt guilty about the accident. After all, he was alive—and Damian was dead. Wouldn't that be a painful realisation for him if he had been

Damian's closest friend for years?

Was his unconscious trying to make amends by stealthily assuming some of Damian's personality? If he was copying Damian's work, haunting the woods and river banks which Damian had loved so much, visiting his tower studio, showing bitter hostility and at the same time a savage sexual attraction towards her, it might all add up to a subconscious wish to give Damian back his life, live for him.

She screwed the top back on to the bottle of oil and carefully put it down, her movements studied, trying to calm herself because what was happening inside her head was so disturbing.

Was she the one who was unbalanced? Was it crazy even to consider the idea? She had to face the fact that she felt guilty, too. Ever since she heard about Damian's death she had been in a state of mental turmoil. What about those terrible dreams she had had? What about what happened the night she arrived in Flamboise— her complete conviction that someone had held her, kissed her, under the willows, and that it had been Damian?

Damian was dead. He was dead. He couldn't have been on the river bank, he couldn't have kissed her. Had anyone been there? Had she imagined the whole thing?

Or had that been Yves, too? That would explain why Chantal had denied that anyone had been there, but it would also imply that Chantal knew that her husband was behaving oddly.

One of us is unbalanced, Elizabeth told herself—the question is: is it me or Yves de

Lavalle? Is all this happening in my mind—or in his?

Leaning over, she picked up her book put her sunglasses on, and forced herself to read a few chapters. The sun became much hotter, she moved her chair back into the shade of a cherry tree and glanced at her watch. It was almost noon, she must go in soon and get herself a light lunch. There was plenty of salad in the fridge, she wasn't hungry, she would have some cheese and salad.

Half an hour later she gathered up her belongings and went back into the house, her body heavy and sleepy after the hours in the sunshine. She showered, put on a loose green cotton tunic which just reached her knees, and went back down to the kitchen to get some lunch.

She carefully mixed a fresh dressing of oil, lemon and vinegar and tossed the lettuce in it, added chicory and endive and cucumber and peppers to make a crisp green salad, then sat down to eat it with a selection of French cheeses; goat's cheese flavoured with herbs, smooth Brie and a very strong Camembert, so ripe it was almost oozing off the plate.

After lunch Elizabeth made some coffee and drank it slowly, listening to the silence in the house and the warm breathing of the garden; the rustle of trees, the birdsong, the faint whisper of the wind. The heat was too intense to go out now she decided to take a siesta and stretched out on the couch.

When she woke up again it was late afternoon, the blue shadows from the trees lay along the walls and the heat had slackened. Elizabeth yawned, getting up, and felt restless. She looked at her watch. Four o'clock—what time would the others get back from Angers? They were having lunch there and would no doubt do some shopping after that. Bored with her own company suddenly, she decided to walk to the village and buy some more postcards. She had sent one to Max already, but she should send some to her friends in the firm.

Flamboise was a small village with one main street which wound narrowly uphill. The sixteenth-century church stood on a tiny square opposite the policeman's house and a bar. There were also a boulangerie, a charcuterie and a pork butcher's shop within a few yards of each other. The square was, of course, La Place de la Révolution—every town and village in France has one, just as it has a war memorial close to the church. Flamboise had a stern First World War soldier pointing heavenward with a wreath of fresh flowers laid at his feet, his rifle in his other hand and on the granite plinth the words: Mort Pour La Patrie. There was a bench along the church wall and on it dozed two old men who each opened an eye as Elizabeth walked past.

'*Bonjour, messieurs,*' she said, and they answered warily.

She took her time doing her shopping; bought some postcards at the bar and then sat down to drink a cold chocolate, walked on to the boulangerie and bought some marzipan cakes and some freshly baked bread, still warm from the oven and smelling of heaven.

She took a short cut home, down a lane so narrow that only one car could use it at a time. Deep banks on either side enclosed fields of vine: the lane must be very old, the surface of it had sunk between the thick hedges so that you couldn't see anything of the fields behind them.

She was at the narrowest part of the road when she heard a car coming fast behind her. Glancing round, she saw a small red Renault, and then, with a start of shock, she saw Chantal de Lavalle was driving it. Chantal's face was set rigid in a glare of hostility.

Elizabeth only just had time to leap aside as the car bonnet swept down on her. She crashed sideways into the high bank, her face and hands ripped by sharp thorns and trailing brambles, then fell into the dry ditch at the base of the hedge.

For a moment she lay, face down, trembling. She heard the car screech to a stop a little farther on; the door was flung open and footsteps ran back towards her.

With panic-stricken haste, Elizabeth scrambled to her knees, shaking. Chantal knelt down beside her. She was very pale and she was trembling, too.

'*Mon dieu, je suis désolée, vous savez ... pardonnez-moi ... c'est ...*' The stammered words made little sense, Elizabeth was only guessing at them, then Chantal looked at her face with horrified eyes and said clearly: '*Oh, mon dieu, votre visage! Je suis désolée!*'

'Driving like a crazy idiot,' Elizabeth stammered back angrily. 'I thought you were going to run me down!'

Their eyes met and Chantal flinched, Elizabeth caught an audible breath, going white.

'You were . . .'

'No!' Chantal protested in a high-pitched voice, then incoherently: 'I don't know, I wasn't thinking, I didn't mean . . . no, of course not. I just wasn't thinking, you know—don't you understand?'

Elizabeth found it hard to follow her fast, stuttered French. She got to her feet, swaying dizzily, and Chantal muttered under her breath. She tentatively put an arm around Elizabeth. 'Please, let me look at your face, it is bleeding badly. Oh, what have I done! Are you in pain?'

'I'll be all right,' Elizabeth told her. 'If I could just sit down . . .'

'The car, please,' said Chantal, and guided her over to it, helped her into the passenger seat. Elizabeth leaned forward, her head in her hands, feeling faint, as much from the shock of the accident as from any injury.

Chantal got into the driver's seat and started the engine. 'You must let me take you to the doctor,' she said, and Elizabeth said huskily: 'No! I don't want to see a doctor, I'll be fine in a minute—I'm feeling a bit shaky, that's all.'

'Are you sure?' Chantal asked, looking sideways at her. Elizabeth caught the relief in her voice— Chantal would not want any talk about the accident. If she was charged with driving dangerously she would at the very least lose her licence, she might be heavily fined or even sent to prison for a short time.

'Sure,' Elizabeth said, and a wave of icy coldness

swallowed her and she slumped forward. A few moment's later the car stopped and Chantal bent over her anxiously.

'Are you all right?'

Elizabeth straightened slowly, her head going round. 'I'll be fine in a moment or two,' she whispered, then laughed shortly. 'What I need is a drink!'

Chantal got out of the car and came round to help Elizabeth out, her arm around her waist. It wasn't until Elizabeth had walked in through the open door outside which they had parked that she realised where they were. Chantal had brought her to the Château.

She halted, aware of the damp coldness of the high-ceilinged hall with its stone floor and plastered stone walls. It echoed like a barn, the faded red of the stone hollowed here and there by generations of feet. A few old, leather-seated chairs stood against the walls, but otherwise the enormous room was bare.

'You must sit down,' Chantal urged, moving forward. Elizabeth reluctantly allowed herself to be led along a shadowy corridor whose corners were spidery, dusty webs everywhere. Clearly this part of the Château had not yet been modernised.

The proportions were enormous, the ceilings vaulted overhead, the stone floor echoing with their steps, the windows running from around her waist level to the ceiling, measuring at least ten foot, she decided, with ancient wooden shutters of the same length open on each side of them. Through faintly dusty glass, Elizabeth caught glimpses of a vast courtyard, its stone flags dusted with pale sand, and framing it the façade of the Château, gleaming a creamy gold in the late afternoon sunlight. It was early eighteenth century; built in an E-shape, with the main body of the building flanked on either side by two short wings. She and Chantal, she realised, were walking through the left hand wing.

They passed through a series of high, ancient doors closing off each section of the corridor, and Elizabeth was aware of other doors to the left of her, opening into rooms, no doubt. Halfway along the corridor, they passed the base of a narrow, winding flight of wooden stairs leading to the upper floor. At the foot of it stood a massive old cabinet, with brass handles to the drawers in it, and on top of it a Chinese bowl, copper, she suspected, with the bluish-green verdigris patina of age.

By now she was lost, bewildered, disorientated by the sheer size of the place, but they turned a corner and Chantal opened a door into a bright, modern bathroom.

'Your face needs attention,' she said. 'Then I'll get you that drink.'

Elizabeth washed her face and hands, brushed some streaks of grass and mud off her green cotton tunic and they went into a room beyond. It was a comfortably furnished sitting-room with carpets on the floors and elegant silky wallpaper on the walls. Light flooded into it from the windows.

'Sit down, please,' said Chantal.

Elizabeth sat down on one of the Queen Anne chairs, upholstered on back and seat in yellow satin brocade, with the splayed claw feet painted white with a touch of gilding here and there. They were not chairs meant to relax in—they forced you to sit bolt upright. Opposite her were the windows, hung with curtains whose material matched the brocade on the chair. It was a spacious, light room; a mirror hung on one wall, doubling the image of the room it reflected, and in it she saw her own pale face swimming and beyond it the faintly moving branches of a cedar in the garden. Despite the sunlight, Elizabeth felt just as lost and strange as she had in the shadowy corridor—there was something unreal about this room, too.

'Brandy,' Chantal said shortly, putting a glass into her hand.

Elizabeth sipped, coughing as the heat of the smooth spirit hit her throat, and the other girl watched her, her sallow skin without colour and her dark eyes uneasy.

'I didn't mean to run you down—I didn't!' she burst out.

'It looked like it,' Elizabeth said, and Chantal flinched. 'Your face was frightening,' Elizabeth added bluntly. 'I saw it before I jumped...' She had read intention in it; Chantal's eyes had been harsh with hatred, the car had leapt forward with a roar of acceleration, almost flung at her, as though Chantal was using it as a weapon.

'I was surprised to see you,' Chantal explained, running a trembling hand through her long black hair. It hung on either side of her disturbed face, straight and silken, a little fringe brushing her temples.

'Surprised?' Elizabeth repeated. 'Angry, don't you mean?'

'That's libel,' Chantal stammered. 'Saying I tried to run you down ... it's a lie, and if you repeat it I'll have to contact my lawyers.'

Elizabeth tilted the brandy glass to her mouth and let some more of the smooth, mellow fire run down her throat. The fumes made her head swim, her skin grew flushed.

'You hate me, don't you?'

Chantal stared at her, lips tight. She didn't answer, and Elizabeth drank some more brandy, staring at her. Yves's wife hated her, she knew that, she hadn't needed the proof of seeing Chantal's face behind that steering wheel half an hour ago. It hadn't really surprised her when Chantal drove straight at her, accelerating. It had frightened her, shocked her, but it had not been a surprise. They had only met twice, but each time she had felt something hostile in the other girl; it showed in the eyes, in the tension of the mouth, just as it showed with Yves himself.

'What have I ever done to make a stranger hate me?' she said to herself rather than to Chantal.

A glitter came into the other girl's eyes, giving them the hard brilliance of polished jet. 'What have you done? I'll tell you what you did. Damian was my husband's closest friend, did you know that? Did you think we didn't hear all about you?' She took a step closer, her hands clenched at her sides, staring. 'Over and over again he told us ... drunk, sober ... he was so miserable after you went. You didn't care, though, did you? You drove him mad with jealousy, you destroyed him!' Her voice had risen little by little until she was almost yelling the last words. 'You caused that crash! It was you, you killed him. Don't you have nightmares about it? How can you sleep knowing ... I have nightmares. I wake up screaming. Flames, flames!' She put her hands over her face shuddering, her body trembling so violently that Elizabeth got up to catch hold of her, thinking she was going to fall. Chantal jumped as she felt her touch and pushed her away with angry force, weeping.

'Don't touch me! I couldn't bear to have *you* touch me!'

Elizabeths's hands fell back. She looked away, wishing she knew what to say to the girl. 'I'm sorry.' It was feeble, lame, she winced even as she said it, and Chantal looked round, laughing bitterly.

'You're sorry? Sorry? My God! Is that all you can say? Do you know how long I'd been married before the crash? Just over a year—we were so happy, I was almost scared, we were so happy, it didn't seem possible to feel like that. We had everything we wanted, it was too good to be true.' She looked around the room, her hand out, gesturing. 'All this ... a dream, my dream. He got it for me, did you know that? He liked Paris, he'd always lived there. It was me who wanted to move out into the country, and when we were staying with Damian and saw this old place I fell in love with it. It was a ruin, falling down—but I loved it and Yves bought it for me, and we were in heaven here.'

Elizabeth bit her lip, listening. 'You will be again,' she murmured uneasily, and Chantal looked at her with that bitter hostility.

'No,' she said. 'I'll never be happy like that again. You killed our dream.'

Elizabeth flinched. 'When he's stronger . . .' she stammered. 'He'll get over the crash some day, I'm sure he will.' She felt sick with guilt, remembering Yves de Lavalle's lovemaking in the old tower. She had forgotten then that he was married, that they barely knew each other. She despised herself—how could she have let him touch her like that? Did Chantal guess? Or did she know? Had Yves told her anything?

Chantal turned abruptly and walked away. She opened the door. 'If you feel better now, I'll drive you home,' she said stiffly.

'Thank you,' said Elizabeth. She followed Chantal down the corridor which was growing dusky as the sun set behind the woods which ran between the Chateau and the river. Chantal walked very quickly, unsteadily. In her lilac-printed white summer dress she looked fragile, so slender she might have been a ghost flitting along the corridor.

As they walked out of the building a grey moth brushed Elizabeth's cheek and she gave a stifled cry of surprise.

Chantal looked round, eyes wide. 'What is it?'

'A moth,' Elizabeth said, and tried to smile.

Chantal's mouth indented impatiently, she opened the car and Elizabeth got into it. They had parked, she saw now, on a sandy drive which ran away from the Château under bending lime

trees with on one side of the drive a green stretch
of parklands and on the other a darkening wood.
The insistent chirp of crickets sounded around
the Château, somewhere a dog barked, and as
Chantal switched on her headlights to drive away
Elizabeth saw some rabbits scampering into the
trees.

'Isn't the Château too big for just the two of
you?' she asked, and Chantal stared straight
ahead, her chin lifted defiantly.

'We like it.'

'You like it,' Elizabeth said, half to herself. Did
Yves really like it here? Or had he bought it
simply to please his new wife and did he now
regret the decision?

Chantal swung the red car as she reached a
corner in the drive. Elizabeth saw her eyes flick
to the driving mirror, watched Chantal glancing
back at the creamy stone of the Château which
was being eaten up by evening mists creeping in
from the wood and the river. Chantal's mouth
softened, her face grew dreamy, the dark eyes
held an enchanted lustre.

'It is beautiful,' Elizabeth said softly, watching
intently.

'Yes,' Chantal breathed like someone talking
about a lover, a glow in her face.

'Does Yves feel like that about it?' Elizabeth
asked, and the other girl's eyes switched back to
her, hardening. Chantal's whole face tightened,
her eyes grew cold, like polished stones, little
glints of angry light in them.

'He's my business, he's still a sick man, he
doesn't know what he's doing or saying some-

times. All those operations left him very weak, he may look strong and fit, but he isn't, he ... he isn't himself. Stay away from him, I don't want him to be reminded of Damian.' She was talking in a hoarse, angry voice, driving too fast with her eyes on the shadowy road. 'Do you hear? Stay away from Yves, from both of us. Go back to England and don't ever come back!'

CHAPTER SEVEN

THAT weekend, Teddy Hertford drove them over to Le Lude to see the famous Spectacle—a kind of historical pageant—at the château there. It stood high on a rock above the main street running through the small village, a castle out of the storybooks; with a slate blue roof and pinnacles to the towers, it had been built as a medieval fortress to guard the river Loir and its present peaceful air, dreaming in the sunlight, gave no hint of the bitter fighting which had taken place there long ago.

The town was crowded with visitors, but Teddy had booked a table for dinner at the best local restaurant, and they ate a leisurely meal before seeing the waterside pageant performed with a backing of dramatic sound and changing light.

Teddy read the menu gleefully. 'I've promised myself one really good French meal before I go back,' he told them.

Vicky sat with her eyes fixed on the menu and didn't look up. Aunt Fleur looked at her quickly, then at Teddy. 'When do you leave?' she asked him, and he shrugged.

'Middle of next week—I'm running out of bread.'

'Bread?' Aunt Fleur repeated, baffled.

He grinned at her. 'Money.'

'Oh,' she said.

'He thinks it sounds hip,' Vicky told her aunt, still without looking up. 'Makes the students feel he's on their side. Except that it's so dated it's positively antique, and he doesn't teach history.'

Teddy blew her a kiss. 'Aren't you a little sweetheart?'

'Just dripping with sweetness and light,' she agreed, then looked up and laughed at him suddenly. 'Sorry, but it's true.'

Teddy grimaced. 'I suppose so—but I'd still like you to come outside and let me beat the hell out of you.'

'Into S. and M,' are we?' Vicky mocked, and Aunt Fleur glanced at Elizabeth, her eyebrows raised.

'I sometimes get the feeling they talk a different language.'

Teddy tapped Vicky's menu with one finger. 'Just order and shut up, will you, angel?'

She saluted, a hand smartly at right angles to her forehead. 'Sir!'

Elizabeth watched her sister uncertainly—what was going on between her and Teddy? At times she felt sure that Vicky was in love with him, at others she decided her suspicions were way off course. Of course, it was none of her business and Vicky wouldn't thank her for her interest. Vicky had made no attempt to confide in her, and Elizabeth respected her sister's privacy but couldn't help speculating. Watching her and Teddy, she found it impossible to guess how either of them felt, but one thing was crystal clear: they were both very much aware of each other, they knew each other very well, and whenever Elizabeth saw them together she felt a distinct prickle of atmosphere, even if she couldn't be certain what it was she was picking up, or from whom.

After a delicious meal of home-made terrine of rabbit and prunes, followed by a tiny piece of bream in a white wine sauce and then quail stuffed with cherries, they had some cheese and skipped the dessert, finishing with some very good coffee, because time was getting short and they did not want to miss the performance at the Château.

It was quite a long drive back from Le Lude after the performance, and they were all tired. Elizabeth stared out of the window of the car watching the darkness of the fields and woods stretching away behind the road. Aunt Fleur had dozed off; she heard her gently snoring, a muffled little whistle of noise beside her. She glanced at the front seat and saw that Vicky's head had slipped sideways and was on Teddy's shoulder. Her sister was breathing softly, rhythmically. The car halted at a traffic light and Teddy glanced back and smiled at Elizabeth, silently mouthing a comment.

'She's asleep.'

Elizabeth smiled back at him, nodding. He was a nice man, she liked him very much, but if he hurt Vicky she would feel like tearing him limb from limb, although that was stupid—Teddy had done nothing so far as she could see to make Vicky fall in love with him, he was casual and friendly with her, no more. It wouldn't be his fault if Vicky got hurt; love was something too personal and private for those outside that magic circle to understand, how could anyone else judge what was really happening and if one of a pair was to blame? Anyway, she decided, who said Vicky was in love? Vicky hadn't said so, Vicky hadn't breathed a word. It was all guesswork on her part and she could be wrong—trying to guess the truth about a personal relationship was like trying to do algebra when you only knew half the symbols.

When the car stopped outside Aunt Fleur's cottage Vicky sat up, yawning, very flushed.

'Are we here?' Aunt Fleur asked, peering out.

'Home again, home again, clippety-clop,' said Vicky in a sing-song nursery chant.

'Baby!' said Teddy, smiling at her.

Elizabeth got out of the car, feeling distinctly like a gooseberry, and Aunt Fleur joined her on the path. 'Goodnight, thank you, Teddy,' they called without looking round, and Teddy called back: 'Goodnight.'

Elizabeth went up to her room and got undressed and into bed. She lay in the darkness feeling very lonely. The way Teddy and Vicky had smiled at each other had made her envy them. It had reminded her of Damian—and she did not want to remember. It hurt too much, not least because it had been she who walked out on him; she had ended their affair herself and even if she had had what had seemed like good reasons at the time, nevertheless, now she wished vainly that she could turn back the clock and begin again.

She couldn't, Damian was dead, he would never come again, but knowing that did not end the hopeless ache of longing inside her. The very impossibility made her burn with angry frustration, with the desperate impatience of someone who knows there is no hope and yet cannot abandon it. Ever since she heard that he was dead, she had felt like someone locked inside an escape-proof room: she mentally beat on the doors and walls, screaming silently, she clutched at any tiny straw of hope, however crazy. He couldn't be dead, Damian couldn't die, she couldn't bear it. She felt all the time that there had to be some way out of this black misery, if only she could find it. She could not accept the fact that he was dead and she couldn't rest while she kept hoping it wasn't true.

Her mood kept changing. One minute she told herself to be sensible and believe it. Damian is dead, she told herself. There's no possibility of mistake. A dull quiet would fall on her raw nerves and she would feel calm and grey, drained. Then from somewhere inside her mind the tormenting whispering would begin again ... is he dead? How can he be? If only ...

'If' was a word which haunted her. If only she hadn't left him in the first place, if only she had been here with him, if only, if only ...

That night she had her recurring nightmare again—it was always the same; she was in a hotel full of people whose faces she didn't recognise but whom she felt she knew. She was running down long, shadowy corridors, looking for Damian. He was there, she knew he was, always just around the next corner, but although she kept seeing him in the distance or being told he was in the next room, she never caught up with him. She was desperate, she couldn't give up, she ran and ran, feeling people stare at her and not caring what they thought.

Then he was there, his back to her, and she gave a wild gasp of relief and joy and exclaimed: 'Damian!'

He turned and it was him, then his face began to melt and dissolve into new features and it was not Damian, it was Yves de Lavalle, and he laughed and caught hold of her, bending towards her, softly whistling Damian's favourite folk song.

Elizabeth screamed and woke up, sitting up in the bed, her arms flailing to beat him off.

The room was full of the first light of dawn; pale, grey, haunting. She put her hands over her face, shuddering.

A second later she heard the whistling again and her blood ran cold. Was she still dreaming? She pressed her shaking hands against her face and felt the reality of skin on skin, bone against hard bone. Her hands ran up into her hair and clenched in it, and it hurt. The pain proved she was awake, but she still heard the soft, far-off whistling, and a second later she was out of the bed and running to the window.

She flung it open, leaning out. The garden was coming into view, a bush here, a flower there, looming through drifting river mist, the leaves dripping wet. Elizabeth stared desperately, eyes flashing in all directions. There was nobody

there. All she saw was mist and damp greenery.
But she heard the whistling even now—slowly
fading as though the whistler was walking away,
yet she heard no sound of footsteps.

Had it been Yves? Or had she been imagining
it?

She ran to the wardrobe and pulled down some
clean jeans, a warm yellow sweater and anorak.
Letting herself out of the house as quietly as she
could, she walked along the narrow roads. There
was no one about; no cars on the road, no sign of
light in any of the isolated houses she passed. She
walked until she was exhausted, her mind too
restless for her to go back yet.

Slowly the mist drifted away and the sun
swum up out of it, the sky turned blue and the
birds began to sing, a few cars passed her, she
saw the baker taking down his shutters, a
fragrant odour of newly baked bread coming
from his shop.

'*Bonjour, m'mselle*,' he called and she stopped
to buy some croissants and a loaf.

She met Aunt Fleur as she got back to the
house, her bag clutched in her hand. 'Elizabeth
... where on earth ...' Aunt Fleur began and
Elizabeth smiled too brightly and handed her the
bread.

'I woke up early and felt energetic—I thought
I'd save you the walk to the village to get bread.'

'How nice of you,' Aunt Fleur said uncertainly,
watching her. 'Are you quite well, dear? You
seem pale.'

I'm haunted, Elizabeth thought, but she said
aloud: 'I had a headache—too much wine at

dinner last night, I suspect. It's better now, though. A long walk always clears your head.'

There was a clatter of hooves on the road behind them, and they both turned and saw Chantal on her black horse trotting down towards the river. Her hair was tied up behind her under a black velvet cap, she wore jodhpurs and a thick-ribbed white sweater which clung to her slender waist, making her look thinner than ever.

'Good morning, Chantal,' said Aunt Fleur, and Chantal nodded, reining the horse to stand beside them. She glanced at Elizabeth, eyes cold.

'You're still here? When does your holiday end?'

'Next week,' said Elizabeth, feeling like adding: Sorry!

'How is Yves, my dear?' Aunt Fleur asked, and Chantal detached her gaze from Elizabeth and looked back at Aunt Fleur, defiance in the way her head moved.

'Fine!' She hurled the word at them, dared them to question it. 'We'll probably be going on holiday to the south soon, I thought it would be fun to spend a week or two at Antibes.'

'That sounds nice, it would do Yves good to have a holiday in the sun,' Aunt Fleur said, and Chantal nodded, touched her knee to the horse's side and moved off, saying a brusque: '*Au revoir.*'

Elizabeth stared after her, knowing that Chantal had told them about the holiday for her benefit; she was taking Yves away. From the danger of seeing Elizabeth too often? Was Chantal afraid of losing him? Elizabeth felt her face burning. Chantal had every right to resent

her. She didn't know just how much she had to
resent. Elizabeth despised herself for what had
happened in the tower that day. She had
forgotten Yves was married, but he hadn't,
surely? What had gone wrong between him and
his wife since the accident? Had he fallen out of
love during his long months of pain? If that
was true, no wonder Chantal was unhappy and
angry. Until that car crash, she and Yves had
been in love, happy together in their château
and their new life. The crash had destroyed all
that, it had not only killed Damian, it had
killed the Yves de Lavalle who had been deeply
in love with his young wife. Chantal's whole
life had fallen apart. Who could blame her for
being bitter?

'What did Chantal do before she was married?'
she asked Aunt Fleur idly as they walked back
into the house.

'I can't remember,' Aunt Fleur said, then
stopped, smiling. 'Yes, I do—she worked in one
of the fashion houses, I think. A model?' She
thought, frowning. 'No, I think she was a buyer,
a trainee buyer. I'm not quite sure. Why?'

'I just wondered,' Elizabeth said. 'She seems so
much at home here in the country, I thought she
must be a country girl.'

'I believe she was,' Aunt Fleur agreed. 'She
rides beautifully, doesn't she? Born to sit in a
saddle. Good with dogs, too. It's nice to see
someone in their right setting—I can't imagine
Chantal anywhere but at the Château, it's the
perfect background for her.'

'Lucky for her to marry a man with so much

money. I wonder what Yves's family thought of him leaving Paris—do they live there?'

'Oh, yes. I met his parents once. They seemed very pleasant, but Chantal doesn't get on with them, I think they disapproved of Yves giving up the bank. His father's a formal sort of man. His mother's dead now, she had a stroke just after the accident—the shock, I suppose, poor woman— and the father has withdrawn since her death. He hasn't visited his son for months. Very sad. I hate to see a family break up like that.'

'Was Yves their only son?'

'Only son, yes, but they have two daughters. One of them lives in Africa with her husband, the other is in America. I remember that they both flew home when their mother died. Chantal mentioned that they'd visited Yves in hospital. One of them was pregnant at the time, she almost lost her baby with all the trouble and travelling— but it turned out all right, it was a boy and they called it Yves. Chantal was rather annoyed—she wanted her own first boy to be Yves.'

'No reason why he still can't,' Elizabeth said absently, aware of an odd feeling inside her. It felt like jealousy, but why should she be jealous at the idea of Chantal having a baby? Envy, perhaps—she would feel much happier now if she had had Damian's baby. What would it have looked like? Black hair and eyes, a strong nose and chin . . . she sighed. Pipe dreams—she had to come to terms with the fact of Damian's death, and she wouldn't do that by imagining what his child would have looked like.

That afternoon, she and Vicky went for a walk

through the woods with Teddy, who kept darting off to look at plants which caught his eye. Elizabeth walked on, leaving her sister to wait for him. Glancing back she saw them standing close together, Teddy holding a flower in his hand, showing it to Vicky, who touched the petals with a careful finger, then looked up and smiled at him. Teddy lifted the flower and trailed it delicately over Vicky's mouth.

Elizabeth turned away and walked on, feeling she was an intruder. It was a very warm afternoon, the river murmured behind the trees, sighing like a human being. She reached the bank and stretched out beneath a shady oak, closing her eyes to enjoy the sun on her face. She was wearing brief white shorts and a halter-necked top which cut off above the midriff and left most of her bare. Her skin had a new, smooth golden tan after days of sun and fresh air. At least she would go back to New York looking as though she had had a good holiday.

She would just have time to spend a few more days with her family and then her holiday would be over and she would be flying back to America. It seemed so far away, as she lay there on the bank, bedded on short grass, listening to the river, and the oak leaves dancing on the hot air. At a distance she could hear Teddy and Vicky talking quietly; they were wandering through the trees, she heard twigs crack and fern rustling.

There was a new sound closer at hand, footsteps on the grass, breathing. She felt someone bending next to her, something touched her face and she smiled without opening her eyes. 'Vicky, that tickles . . .'

Cool petals brushed her face, trailed down to her smiling mouth. She lifted her lids sleepily and at first saw only a deep, blue blur, a flower flicking across her open eyes, then she saw Yves de Lavalle's face behind it, and her whole body jerked in shock.

'Some people call it monkshood,' he said inconsequentially. 'Some call it aconite.'

Huskily, with anger, Elizabeth snapped: 'And some call it wolf's bane!' That was the name she knew it by: it was very familiar to her, that long green stem with spikes of dark blue flowers on each side of it. Damian's favourite flower, he had drawn it over and over again, trying to catch the exact colour of the petals. It grew in the woods in summer, sometimes you missed it in the blue-black shade of the trees.

'A good name for it,' said Yves, smiling, his white teeth predatory, his eyes the patient, stalking, unreachable eyes of the wolf, and she shivered.

'It's poisonous,' she said, defying him. 'Did you know that?'

'Deadly,' he agreed, but he did not look at the flower, he looked at her slowly with intent, dark eyes which moved over her curved golden body in the brief shorts and even briefer sun top. 'But beautiful,' he said softly, and drew the long stem with its silky flowers down her body in a deliberate caress, from her pulsing throat over her half-naked breasts, the smooth midriff and onwards to the long, slim legs.

Elizabeth put out an angry hand and knocked
the flower away. 'Don't touch me! Go back to
your wife—she wants you, I don't!'

'Liar,' he said, his voice husky, but she caught
a flicker of emotion in his face—bewilderment?
uncertainty? She wasn't sure which.

'You're married, and I don't get involved with
married men,' she said bitingly. 'Your wife's
unhappy enough already, and who can blame
her? I'm sorry for her.'

'Chantal is nothing to do with this,' he said,
and he was angry too now, she saw dark red
colour lying along his cheekbones.

'She's your wife! She's had a hard time, I don't
want to make it any harder.' Elizabeth sat up,
would have got to her feet if he hadn't yanked her
back, held her arms, staring into her face.

'I can't stop thinking about you,' he broke out,
as though accusing her.

'Try.' She kept her eyes on him because she
was afraid to look away, she felt she had to watch
him and anticipate any move he made.

'Were you ever in love with Damian, or was it
all on his side?' he asked, his lips twisting wryly.

'I was in love with him,' she said flatly, with
pain.

'Then why . . .' He was frowning, staring, his
eyes probing her face.

'Damian's jealousy was impossible to live
with—it was reasonless. I never gave him any
cause to be jealous, there were no other men
except in his mind—if I so much as spoke to a
man he blew his top. I couldn't take any more of
it, it frightened me.' Elizabeth spoke rapidly, her

voice husky, she wanted him to believe her, she had to make him see that whatever Damian had said to him was warped, couldn't be believed. 'He was so intense, he lived on mountain tops—most of us live down in the nice safe valleys,' she said, with bitter humour. 'Damian lived with winds and an air so high with oxygen that ordinary people couldn't breathe it.' She smiled shakily. 'Me, for instance—my lungs couldn't take Damian's air. I felt drunk, lightheaded, and it scared me.'

'That's how I feel,' said Yves, 'when I see you.'

'Don't,' Elizabeth muttered, but he wasn't even listening, she could see it in his face, he was staring at her mouth and breathing audibly, and she heard her own breathing quicken, her stomach clenched in sudden, fierce excitement.

'Don't!' she said again, sharply, moving away, and he tightened his grip on her arms and threw her backwards on to the warm grass. She turned her head sideways to evade his searching mouth, the blades of grass pricked like spears on her flushed cheek. He was lying on top of her, his weight pinning her, she couldn't get up.

'I want you—God, I want you,' he muttered, and she gasped in shock, her mouth parted, then his lips touched hers and flame ran through her; she was burning, her mouth opened thirstily and she moaned with ecstasy. Eyes tightly shut, she wound her arms round him because she needed to feel his body melting into her own, the close pressure of his weight was a satisfaction so intense it took her breath away, left her drowning in feeling. Last time she had felt like this, she hadn't been capable of thought, the emotion possessing her had been too violent, but it couldn't be emotion. She barely knew him, what she did know of him she didn't like. Emotion did not flare up in an instant, like flame running through dry grass. She knew what this was and she hated it yet couldn't help herself.

He was married, and he hated her even if he did want her. You can hate and desire at the same time, Elizabeth knew that. Oh, yes, she thought dazedly, you can hate and desire at the same time, and she wanted him with a wild need which made her whole body shudder and burn. Yves was trembling, too, she felt the heat in him; he moved his lips down her throat and his face was so hot she flinched from it.

'I've got to have you or I'll go mad,' he muttered, his hands touching her hungrily. 'You're a faithless little bitch, but I'm hooked on you, I can't get you out of my mind, night and day . . .'

Suddenly Elizabeth was stiff with tension, her body went ice-cold in shock. 'What?' she whispered, but he wasn't listening, he was burying his face between her breasts, groaning. She had a sensation of *déjà vu* so abrupt it made her head swim. Those words . . . that voice . . .

What's happening to me? Am I trapped in some nightmare? Damian had said that to her two years ago, almost word for word, and in a voice which was almost identical. Yves was kissing her bare midriff, a hand on the zip of her shorts, he seemed unaware that she had gone cold on him.

She sat up, jack-knifing with force, and pushed him away.

'Why are you doing this to me? Is it some sort of mental torture? Are you hoping to drive me crazy? Is that it? Well, you won't succeed, I'm not going to let you send me round the bend! I know what you're doing, but it won't work.'

He had sat up and was staring at her, his face blank. She glared at him, her mouth shaking, her face white.

'You're not Damian! You think you'll make me go mad, don't you? Do you think I can't work out what you're doing? Whistling his favourite song, faking his sketches, talking the way he did.' She looked at the flattened grass and saw the blue flowers of wolf's bane, their petals crushed under her body a moment ago. Reaching over, she picked up the long green stem and flung it far away towards the river. It fell into the water and began to drift away with the tide. 'You knew Damian loved wolf's bane, he was always drawing it. He was your best friend for years, I know that. You blame yourself because he died and you didn't, but you can't bear that guilt, can you? You have to find someone else to take the blame, you can't live with it any more. And I'm the obvious scapegoat, aren't I? You can't punish yourself for surviving when Damian didn't, but you can punish me. He told you all about me, and you think I deserve punishment anyway, don't you? It wasn't hard, I suppose, to work out ways of scaring me—clever little conjuring tricks, like faking the drawing of me by the river. It isn't hard for you to imitate Damian's drawing, anyone can fake someone else's way of doing a simple sketch, and you really knew Damian so well, didn't you? You knew how he worked, thought, talked—did he tell you how he used to talk to me, too? What else did he tell you?' She stopped talking, her face very hot, staring at him. Had Damian told him how she liked to make love, what turned her on? Did he know where to touch her, how to kiss her, what to whisper?

The dark secrets of the lover's mind should never be betrayed—had Damian betrayed her?

At that moment they both heard voices, laughter, the sound of people walking through the trees only a few feet away.

Yves got to his feet, brushing grass off his trousers. He looked at her briefly, harshly, in a strangely intent way—and then he was gone, walking fast along the river bank until he had vanished behind the trailing branches of a willow.

'Oh, there you are,' Vicky said breathlessly, as she pushed through a gap between a holly bush and an oak. 'Where on earth did you get to? Don't tell me you've been peacefully sunbathing all this time while we've been hunting high and low for you in the woods? I'm scratched to blazes, we got into a clump of gorse and couldn't get out without a struggle.'

'Why do women exaggerate?' Teddy demanded, and Vicky pushed him, laughing.

'Next time you want to take me plant-hunting we'll to to Kew!'

'Where's your spirit of adventure?' Teddy asked, flinging himself down on the grass with a sigh of contentment.

'Back there among the gorse bushes,' said Vicky, joining him. She turned to look at Elizabeth, smiling, apparently unaware that anything was wrong. 'It's lovely down in the woods today but safer to stay at home,' she sang loudly.

'A picnic,' Teddy said. 'What a great idea! You go back and pack a nice hamper while Liz and I watch the dragonflies ... see, Liz, there's an enormous one—look at those wings, run up for him by Yves St Laurent himself, I'd say.'

Elizabeth lay down again and closed her eyes. Vicky was teasing Teddy, her voice dancing with happiness. Elizabeth envied her and felt ill, her head ached and she wanted to be back in New York with the tidal roar of traffic and the police whistles and permanent rattle of drills from the omnipresent workmen tearing down or raising buildings. New York renewed itself daily, one day you went to work and there was a bank on the corner of the block. A week later it had gone and there was a hole in the ground full of men in work helmets, drilling away. Before you knew where you were there was a new skyscraper rearing itself up to the clouds. At times Elizabeth had wondered if hell was a little like that—always restless, never at peace. Now she yearned for those noisy streets.

CHAPTER EIGHT

The following evening, Aunt Fleur invited some of her friends to a cold buffet which was served in the garden. So far, Elizabeth and Vicky had only met a few of their aunt's friends—several times while they were shopping with Aunt Fleur in the village or the nearest market town they had run into women from Flamboise and been introduced, made polite conversation for a moment or two.

'Do you have much of a social life?' Elizabeth had asked her aunt curiously, and Aunt Fleur had laughed.

'Not so much in the summer while there's so much to do—but in the winter we visit for coffee and have dinner parties. It isn't so easy for me, I have no husband now, so I make an odd number at dinner. There was a time . . .' she broke off, smiling, and Vicky grinned at her, leaping to an immediate conclusion.

'Tried to matchmake, did they?'

'Something like that,' Aunt Fleur said ruefully.

'Every spare bachelor trotted out?' Vicky teased. 'But you weren't biting, is that it?'

Aunt Fleur made a wry face at her. 'You're a wicked child, that tongue of yours will cut you if you aren't careful!' Then she had said thoughtfully: 'While you two are here, I might give a little party, I owe hospitality to most of my friends.'

'Marvellous!' exclaimed Vicky, clapping her hands. 'I love parties, I'm a party person.'

'One way of describing you,' Elizabeth murmured, and got a cushion thrown at her.

Teddy had been invited—it was his last evening in France and he warned them that he would have to leave the party quite early so as to get a good night's sleep before he set off to drive back to the Channel ports. Aunt Fleur had invited Chantal and Yves, too, but she only mentioned that to Elizabeth after a phone call from Chantal. Elizabeth was at the table eating her croissant and sipping hot chocolate—Vicky was still in bed, she never got up early in the morning during holiday times. The phone rang; Aunt Fleur went to answer it, and came back a few moments later, her face wry.

'That was Chantal—they won't be here tonight after all.'

Elizabeth stiffened. 'I didn't know you'd invited them.'

'Didn't I tell you? Oh, yes, I included them as a matter of courtesy, although frankly I didn't expect them to come. I'm not surprised to get a call from Chantal to excuse them.' Aunt Fleur poured herself some more coffee, very strong, black and sweet. She sipped it, then said: 'Chantal sounded odd, either she's getting a cold or she'd been crying.'

Elizabeth didn't look up, but she felt herself flushing, and she was angry with herself. The sooner she got away from here the better. She didn't want to make Chantal de Lavalle unhappy, she didn't want to get involved with Chantal's husband. She was afraid to look up in case her aunt saw the guilt in her eyes and began to ask unanswerable questions.

'Let's hope a few weeks in the sun will do them both good,' observed Aunt Fleur.

Elizabeth carefully put down her cup of hot chocolate. 'In the sun?'

'They're off to Antibes. Don't you remember? Chantal told us.'

'Oh, yes,' Elizabeth said slowly, pushing a crumb around her plate with one finger. 'So they *are* going, are they?'

'Today,' said Aunt Fleur, getting up and beginning to clear the table. Elizabeth watched her carry the crockery over to the sink and run hot water over them. 'Chantal says Yves suddenly decided to go last night. She rang just as they were leaving, she'd forgotten about my party. They were up at first light, packing, she said. Yves insisted on going right away once he'd made up his mind.' She sighed, shaking her head. 'He's a strange man, what a tragedy that accident was for them—he was never the same again. There's been something odd about him ever since, as if he wan't really there any more. You didn't know him before the accident! Believe me, he's changed so much. Who knows what happens to people when they go through something like that?'

Elizabeth looked at her watch. 'Look at the time—Vicky isn't staying in bed all day. I'll get her up, there's going to be a lot to do for your party, and I don't see why Vicky shouldn't lend a hand.' She hurriedly left the kitchen and went upstairs, but did not go into Vicky's room; she went into her own and stood there, breathing carefully. He had gone and she was relieved, but she felt weak inside, as though her stomach had dropped out and she was empty. She had had to get away before Aunt Fleur noticed anything, she was a noticing woman; Elizabeth spent a lot of time evading her thoughtful eyes.

Aunt Fleur had even noticed a change in Yves; she might not have seen Yves the way Elizabeth had seen him, but Chantal's hostile attitude wouldn't have escaped Aunt Fleur's shrewd gaze. She might place the wrong construction on it, she probably imagined it was entirely because of Damian, but she wouldn't miss it, and if she had ever seen Yves with Elizabeth, even talking at a party, she would have been able to put two and two together and come up with an answer which would have shocked her. Aunt Fleur was old-fashioned, she would be horrified if she suspected that her niece was allowing a married man to make love to her. Elizabeth had always made it an unbreakable rule not to get involved with married men—what had been going on between her and Yves shocked her, too. She despised herself for letting it happen, but whenever she was alone with him she found herself acting in a way which was quite foreign to her. If it hadn't been for all the circumstances surrounding their relationship, she'd have thought she was in love with him, but it wasn't that.

She didn't even know what it was, only that he exerted a hypnotic power over her. When he looked at her, touched her, she felt herself weaken, her mind cloud.

Was it because, although she knew he was deliberately playing on her guilt about Damian, she was still half convinced by his subtle mimicry? When they first met he had been cold, formal, a man whose personality was submerged beneath a polite mask. Gradually, without her realising what was happening, that icy formality had been shed and from behind the mask had sprung the personality of Damian. Yves had made love to her with the stormy wildness she remembered all too well. He had got to her because he touched her the way Damian had touched her, whispered passionate words Damian had once used. How had he known so much about her? How had he known exactly how to reach her? It could only be through Damian. It was crazy, but she couldn't rid herself of the idea that Damian was still reaching out to her, trying to possess her, and using Yves to do it.

Was Yves as much a victim as she was? Did he even know what he was doing? He had looked shaken, stunned, when she accused him on the river bank. He hadn't attempted to deny it, he had just stared at her with fixed, intent black eyes, listening. Was that why he had so abruptly made up his mind to go down south, as Chantal wanted? Was he running because he had suddenly realised what was really happening? Was Yves being haunted by Damian too? Was Damian trying to take him over?

It was an incredible idea, anyone could be excused for thinking she was out of her mind for believing it—but she could see no other way of gathering up all the scattered pieces and forming one definite picture.

There was no doubt about the various bits of evidence—someone had faked Damian's style in those pictures, and who could it be but Yves? Someone kept whistling Damian's favourite tune, she had heard Yves do it. Yves's voice reminded her, his hands reminded her; when he touched her, her body knew him and responded fiercely against all the cool-headed warnings of her brain.

If she kept her eyes closed she could have sworn that the man holding her was Damian, yet when she opened her eyes she saw Yves, and was flung back into bewildered, frightened uncertainty.

At first she had thought Yves was aware of what he was doing, was trying to punish her by pretending to be Damian—but once she had worked that out his power to fool her should have been over, and it hadn't. Yves could not have fooled her into imagining it was Damian kissing her unless at some level of her mind she had been aware that . . .

She broke off, shuddering. It was madness. Was she really so lost to reality that she could even guess at such a thing? Damian was dead. Yves was alive. How could Damian inhabit Yves's body, look at her through Yves's eyes, touch her with his hands?

'I don't believe in ghosts, there's no such thing,' she said aloud, her voice shrill.

'Neither do I,' said a voice behind her, and she jumped violently, swinging round. Vicky stood in the doorway, barefooted, in a cotton nightshirt

which reached the top of her brown thighs. Her
blonde hair was tousled, her face pink, but her
eyes were concerned and worried. 'Talking to
yourself isn't a good sign,' she said lightly. 'You
aren't still seeing ghosts, are you, Liz? Maybe we
shouldn't have come here, there are too many
reminders of Damian around.'

Elizabeth forced a smile. 'I was just going to
wake you up—we've got lots of shopping to do if
Aunt Fleur's party is going to be a success.'

'Do you want to go home, Liz?' Vicky asked,
ignoring that. 'If it's too painful to be in a place
which reminds you of Damian at every turn, we
could start driving back tomorrow and stop off at
Paris for a few days.'

Elizabeth hesitated. 'Aunt Fleur might
think . . .'

'Aunt Fleur's worried about you, too,' Vicky
said quickly.

'Is she?' Elizabeth frowned, half impatient at
that. 'You make me feel very uncomfortable—
have the two of you been talking about me behind
my back?'

'Don't be touchy,' said Vicky. 'You look a bit
like a ghost yourself, even Teddy noticed how
quiet you are, you never seem to be with us.'

Elizabeth said wryly: 'Now that is surprising . . .'

'What is?' Vicky asked, puzzled.

'That Teddy noticed anything except you.'

Vicky went pink. 'Don't be silly!'

'You two can't go around starry-eyed without
it being noticed,' Elizabeth said, smiling.

'Starry-eyed? Do me a favour!' Vicky protested.

'I told you—he's been going around with someone else for years, he hasn't a clue I'm alive.'

'That isn't how I read it. He's practically been living here since we ran into him in Chinon, don't tell me he hangs around all the time to take photos of nettles and ferns. He may have the botany bug, but that isn't what brings him over here almost every day.'

Vicky relaxed, shrugging, and gave a beatific smile. 'He does seem to like me,' she admitted, and Elizabeth laughed.

'Don't be so damned coy!'

'Coy?' Vicky repeated the word, bristling. 'Look, I've been trying to make him see me for months. I got sick of springing up from behind bookcases, out of shop doorways, from under desks . . . it didn't seem to do a thing to him. I gave up in the end. Well, almost,' she finished, grinning, and Elizabeth stared hard at her, thinking back.

'Was that why you wanted to come to France? Because you knew he was going to be in the Loire area?' She saw her sister's rapidly assumed air of innocence and began to laugh. 'It was, wasn't it? You came here in the hope of running into him, I suppose you'd have casually dropped in at his campsite sooner or later if we hadn't seen him when we did.'

'All's fair in love and war,' Vicky shrugged. 'I could tell he wasn't in love with *her*—if he had been he'd have married her long ago. I used to watch them and it stood out a mile that it was just a habit between them. You know how it is—you start seeing someone then you get stuck with them and you can't break it off. It's a bit like watching the telly—you're bored stiff with a programme but you're too bone idle to get up and switch it off. Selective apathy, they call it, don't they? Well, that was what it was with Teddy— sheer apathy. I didn't know how to wake him up.'

'And now he's wide awake?'

Vicky grinned. 'He's certainly seeing me these days, but Teddy isn't the dynamic sort. He's patient and calm and steady, he has a routine for everything. I'm going to have to make myself a habit with him, he won't rush anything, not if I know him. This could take months.' She broke off and looked at Elizabeth with a rueful smile. 'You've done it again, haven't you?'

'Done what?'

'Changed the subject. This started off as a conversation about you—how did we get on to me and Teddy?'

'Why don't you go and take a shower, get dressed and we'll go shopping,' Elizabeth suggested, and Vicky threw up her hands, making a face.

'Okay, okay, have it your own way. If you want to stay here, we'll stay, but I don't like to see you going around looking haunted . . .'

She disappeared into the bathroom and Elizabeth stood staring at the window, watching the faint white wisps of cloud drifting across a blue sky.

Haunted—am I haunted? If everyone can see it in my face, it can't just be in my own mind. I should never have come here, why did I have to see that painting in Max's apartment? If it wasn't for that, I'd still be in New York, believing

Damian to be alive. Her mind jerked violently, like a train jumping a track ... she kept telling herself Damian was dead, but did she believe it? Was anyone dead while you thought of them as alive? If they inhabited a corner of your mind wasn't that a sort of life?

'Are you coming, then?'

Vicky's voice made her start, she looked round incredulously. 'You were quick!' Vicky was dressed, her blonde hair brushed neatly, her face lightly dusted with powder.

'You were miles away, again,' Vicky told her. 'You think too much, that's your trouble.'

'That's my trouble,' Elizabeth agreed, following her down the stairs. She must have been standing there for ten minutes, unmoving, lost in thoughts of Damian. It was worrying to know that your mind just went off, leaving your body standing there like a statue. It made her feel helpless, unable to control her own mind. You didn't ever imagine losing control of your mind, that strange ghost in the machine which is the body, you got used to thinking you ran your own life, and then one day you weren't the boss any more and you didn't know who or what was. It was hair-raising.

They did the shopping, then helped Aunt Fleur cook a variety of party foods—quiches and fruit flans, tiny tartlets full of cream sauce with prawns or mushrooms embedded in it, flaky pastry rich with creamy cheese and chives and some delicious chocolate gateaux with a layer of marrons glacés in the centre of them and thick cream and chocolate on the top.

When Teddy arrived he gloated over the food, his eyes avid. 'It looks delicious, all of it—I shan't know where to start.'

'Pig,' grinned Vicky, pulling him away from the kitchen and all the tempting delicacies. 'Come and help me move some chairs out into the garden. Thank heavens it's a fine evening. I've been praying it wouldn't rain.'

'It won't,' said Teddy, laughing as he looked at the warm blue sky. The sun was very low now, slowly sinking into the dark woods and leaving a golden-red glow in feathered streaks of soft cloud which moved above the trees. 'It's going to be a super evening,' he said confidently.

Aunt Fleur looked after them as they went into the garden and smiled. 'Vicky's in love, isn't it strange how love won't be hidden? She can't take her eyes off him, can she?'

The door bell rang and Elizabeth laughed. 'They're arriving already!'

Flustered, Aunt Fleur began to strip off her cotton apron and Elizabeth smiled at her.

'Don't worry, I'll go.'

Aunt Fleur rushed off to hide her apron and tidy her hair, and Elizabeth went through the little hall to open the door. She had a polite smile ready, but it went as she stared at the man on the doorstep.

'Hi, surprised to see me?' he said, looking amused at her staggered expression.

'Max! *Max!* I don't believe it! What on earth are you doing here?' Elizabeth almost doubted her own eyes, he was the very last person she had expected to see. He looked oddly out of place in France—a firmly muscled, stockily built man with hair which caught the last gleams of the sun on its coppery fire and brown eyes whose smile held satisfaction in her amazement. His lightweight beige suit had American stamped all over it, his shirt was both very expensive and casual, a New Yorker's suit and shirt meant to impress without giving itself airs.

'I'm here to check up on you,' he said bluntly, and looked past her. 'Aren't you going to ask me in?'

'Of course,' said Elizabeth, stepping back and Aunt Fleur appeared in the kitchen doorway, her expression surprised and puzzled.

Flushed, Elizabeth stammered an introduction. 'Max is my boss,' she explained. 'I didn't even know he was in Europe, let alone that he might turn up in the Loire.'

'I hope I'm not interrupting anything,' said Max, glancing from Aunt Fleur's simple but stylish black dress to the classically cut white dress Elizabeth wore. 'You both look very elegant, were you just going out?'

'We're having a party,' Aunt Fleur told him. 'Do stay—it isn't anything elaborate, just a few friends and a cold buffet, we'd love to have you.'

'Thank you,' said Max, looking down at himself. 'But I'm not dressed for a party.'

'You look very smart, don't fish,' Elizabeth said, and Aunt Fleur looked at her watch.

'Will you excuse me, I have so much to do. Elizabeth, will you get Mr Adams a drink?'

Elizabeth took Max into the sitting-room and

put a hand to the whisky bottle. 'Shall I just guess?'

He grinned at her. 'Right first time. I'm not sure I like a woman knowing all about me.'

She poured a finger of whisky into a glass, added soda and handed it to him. 'What are you doing here, Max? It's nice to see you, but what brought you to France?'

'Your postcard,' he said, then swallowed half the whisky.

She frowned, taken aback. 'My postcard?'

'I'm a great one for arithmetic,' Max told her. 'You sent me a postcard from a place called Flamboise. I knew I'd heard that name somewhere before—I couldn't pin it down for an hour or two, then I remembered where I'd heard it. It was where Damian Hayes lived.'

Elizabeth felt herself flushing, her eyes fell. 'Oh.'

'Then I remembered that you'd suddenly decided you needed a holiday immediately after seeing that painting of his in my apartment. I knew something was odd that night. You were as bright as a button when my party started, then you turned faint and had to leave. The next thing I knew you were on a plane to Europe.' He finished his whisky. 'So when I got that postcard and put Damian Hayes and your French holiday together, I started thinking.'

Elizabeth sighed. 'I see. Yes, I came here because of Damian—I knew him a long time ago, it was a shock to hear he'd died. But I'm also here to visit my aunt, and have some sun.' She stopped, frowning. 'How on earth did you get this address?'

'I rang your family in England, said I had to come to France and would like to call by and say hello to you.' Max smiled with satisfaction. 'All very simple, no mystery about it.'

'But why . . .'

'Did I want to see you?' He put down his empty glass. 'I just thought I'd make sure you were okay. I'm counting on you for next season's designs—you're my blue-eyed girl, you know that. If something was wrong with you, I wanted to see what I could do about it.'

'Nothing's wrong,' Elizabeth denied huskily, rather touched, although he made it sound very businesslike and purely a matter of self-interest.

Max tilted a pugnacious chin in her direction and growled: 'Don't give me that, honey. I only had to look at you to know you were in some sort of tailspin. This Hayes—an old flame, was he?'

'Don't bully me, Max,' she said wryly.

'So he *was*,' Max decided. 'I guessed as much. Well, if you're grieving there's only one sure cure for that—you know it.'

Elizabeth considered him, her eyes amused. 'Tell me. You're going to, anyway. It's written all over you.'

'Work,' Max said crisply. 'That old four-letter word. That'll take your mind off the past. You come on back to New York, where you belong, and work your socks off.'

Elizabeth burst into slightly uneven laughter. 'You're priceless, Max, you're absolutely out on your own! Self-interest and kindness combined— a positively lethal combination.'

'But I'm right,' he said, going over to pour himself another whisky as though he owned the place.

Elizabeth gave a husky sigh. 'But you're right, damn you.'

CHAPTER NINE

Max decided to stay on in France for a few days and informed Elizabeth that he was going to let her show him the highspots of the Loire Valley. Whatever Max did, he did with sober dedication, and he had decided to be a tourist, which meant he wanted to see every château on the river, Elizabeth discovered, cramming around five centuries of French history into two or three days' intensive sight-seeing.

He had been something of a hit at Aunt Fleur's party, especially with the middle-aged ladies who had made the majority of the guests. Max had been charming to them, Elizabeth had watched him with amusement as he paid them heavy compliments and got them glasses of wine and bowls of strawberries. His French was minimal and relied largely on some phrase-book which, from overhearing some of his remarks, Elizabeth decided had been published in the Edwardian era. As he slowly wound his way around the crowded terrace he occasionally consulted his little book secretly, one shoulder turned to hide it from the other guests. Elizabeth was longing to have a look at it.

Teddy and Vicky were busy organising the party, pouring wine and handing around food and plates and forks. It had been a warm, calm evening; not a breath of wind, only the cicadas chirping among the trees disturbed the peace. As it grew dark they had an invasion of new, uninvited guests—moths blundered into women's hair and mosquitoes whined as they dive-bombed into the party.

'I think we'll go indoors,' Aunt Fleur said agitatedly, brushing away an enormous grey moth.

It was not long before the party broke up after that—people kept early hours in that district and by midnight the house was silent again, the only evidence of the party which was left was the rows of empty wine bottles and the piles of plates and glasses in the kitchen.

'We'll tidy up tomorrow,' Aunt Fleur decided, yawning as the last guest left. Max had driven away an hour before—he was staying at a small auberge several miles from Flamboise and wanted to get to bed early, having spent all day travelling. Before he left he took Elizabeth aside and said: 'I'll come by early tomorrow and pick you up, then we'll do a few of the châteaux and have lunch.'

'A few of them?' Elizabeth had repeated, laughing. 'Max, they're miles apart. Driving from one to the other will take us hours!'

Max looked discontented. 'Well, we'll see,' he said with obstinate patience. 'I want to try and get to them all while I'm here. I may never come to the Loire again.'

She got up very early next morning and found Aunt Fleur in the kitchen doing the party washing-up. 'Why didn't you wait until Vicky

and I could do that?' protested Elizabeth as her
aunt smiled at her over her shoulder.

'It hasn't taken me long. There's some fresh
coffee. I'm just going to walk to the village to get
some fresh croissants.'

'I'll do that,' said Elizabeth, and went out, in
spite of her aunt's protests. It was a fine, clear
morning, the sun glanced into the woods and lit
them from within so that the trees were haloed in
gold.

Elizabeth drove along the empty, narrow lanes
and bought croissants, rolls and bread, then
drove back to find Vicky up, in jeans and a T-
shirt, helping Aunt Fleur put away the glasses in
their ornate cabinet.

She and Vicky had breakfast, talking about the
party. Vicky glanced at her watch. 'Eight thirty—
Teddy will be well on his way to Calais by now.
He was leaving at crack of dawn.' She shuddered.
'Rather him than me!'

'He seemed to enjoy the party,' said Elizabeth,
and Vicky laughed.

'He ate four of those prawn tartlets, serve him
right if he was up all night with indigestion.' She
finished her hot chocolate and sighed. 'What are
you doing today?'

'Max wants a guided tour of the château
country,' Elizabeth said with a grin. 'Want to
come?'

Vicky linked her arms behind her blonde head,
her curved body provocatively posed. 'No,
thanks, I've seen my last château. I'm just going
to sunbathe from now on—I've had all the
culture I can take.'

Max arrived half an hour later and presented Aunt Fleur with an enormous bouquet of flowers. 'I had a really terrific time last night, *madame*,' he said with an expansive smile. 'Now I'll know what people mean when they talk about French cooking—that was some buffet!'

Aunt Fleur gravely thanked him and said the flowers were very beautiful, she would get them into water at once. Max filled the small house to overflowing, his powerful personality making them all feel breathless. Elizabeth sensed that her aunt was relieved when they left. Max had a large guidebook with him, full of colour photographs of various châteaux. He handed it to her as he started the engine of his hired car. 'I've ringed those I mean to see,' he said, and she knew that having made up his mind he was going to be hard to dissuade.

While they drove, he talked about friends in New York, gleefully reporting gossip which made her laugh. 'I don't believe it!' Max often exaggerated when a story did not seem funny enough, he had no compunction about ripping a reputation to shreds if someone had offended him.

'On my mother's grave,' he said with emphasis, 'it's the sober truth.'

'Max, your mother's not only alive, she's more alive than most people I've ever met—including you!'

He roared with laughter. 'Ain't that the truth? She sent her love, by the way, but she looked worried.' He gave her a sideways look, wicked in its amusement. 'When I told her I was coming

over here to check up on you, she said: why are
you chasing after her, Maxie? You're not such a
big fool you're going to get married again? Isn't
one fortune in alimony enough for you?'

Elizabeth smiled, her eyes dancing. 'And you
said?'

'I said she should mind her own business,
which she won't and never has, of course.'

'Max, your business *is* her business,' Elizabeth
said drily. She knew his mother very well and
admired her, she laughed at her sometimes, but
was very fond of her too. Mrs Adams was small,
almost spherical in shape, and thought she ruled
the world.

'But don't get any ideas,' Max warned. 'I'm
here strictly for business reasons.'

'I know that,' said Elizabeth, amused again.

'But I'm curious,' Max admitted, weaving
through a little cluster of slow-moving cars and
being hooted at with Gallic affront. Ignoring this,
Max went on: 'Why are you over here? How
serious was it between you and this guy Damian
Hayes?'

'Pretty serious,' Elizabeth said lightly.

'What sort of guy was he?' Max asked. He was
fascinated by other people, he probed their
motives and ideas when he met them with the
assiduous determination of an anteater prowling
through tangled undergrowth in search of a meal.

Elizabeth groaned, running a hand over her
smooth blonde hair, her green eyes wry. 'I
wouldn't know where to begin—he was a brilliant
painter . . .'

'I know that stuff,' Max told her. 'I did some

homework on him before I came. I want to know what the man was like, forget the paintings.'

'You and me both,' said Elizabeth, and Max turned his bullet head to stare at her. She smiled with rueful reluctance. 'He was so many things, nobody could accuse him of being simple. Charming, aggressive, funny, wild—I could go on all night and it wouldn't give you any real idea what he was like.'

'Still hung up on him, aren't you, honey?' Max said gently, and she nodded, looking out of the window at the regular lines of vines in the fields on either side of the road.

Max took a hand off the wheel and touched hers. 'I'm sorry, Liz, it's tough. I could give you the old bromide about it soon passing, but I won't. Just hang in there with your teeth gritted.'

She laughed huskily. 'You make it sound like a prizefight!'

'Life often works out like that. My ex left me flat on the canvas, I've still got ringing in the ears.'

She was silent for a while, then asked: 'Max, do you believe in ghosts?'

He looked round at her, frowning. 'Ghosts? Are you kidding?'

She shook her head.

'No, I don't believe in ghosts,' Max said. 'I believe in work and I want to get you back to the States—and fast.'

Over the next two days she spent hours with him, driving from château to château, tramping through elegantly furnished rooms, staring at paintings and statues, walking through the exquisite formal gardens around some of them. Max crossed each château off his list with childish satisfaction, like a schoolboy doing homework piece by piece. He was tireless and absorbed, but Elizabeth knew him too well not to realise that he brought that dogged concentration to everything he did. It was the secret of his success in business.

The weather stayed fine; calm, blue skies, a dazzling sunshine and just enough breeze to make the heat bearable. Each day Vicky wandered into the garden and stretched out in a bikini with a bottle of suntan oil and a pile of magazines and books. She was infuriatingly amused by Elizabeth's envy.

'He's your friend . . .' she smirked when Elizabeth wailed over Max's obsession with sightseeing.

'Boss,' Elizabeth stressed. 'If he was my friend I could tell him to get lost, but you don't argue with Max if you want to keep your job.'

'I think he's rather cute, like a big teddybear.'

'Cute?' Elizabeth repeated. 'He's more grizzly bear than teddy bear, believe me!' She was worn out after two days of touring the Loire Valley with him. 'Thank heavens he leaves tomorrow,' she said. 'I'll just have two days to relax, then we'll be going too.'

Max was in the kitchen with Aunt Fleur, who was demonstrating the right way to mix a French dressing. Elizabeth could hear his deep voice growling. 'I get you, then what?'

Aunt Fleur sounded distracted. 'Then . . . then it's ready to pour over the salad,' she said almost guiltily, as though there ought to be more to it than that.

'Oh, I see,' said Max, sounding disappointed. 'Well,' he said on a long note, 'that's pretty simple,' his tone dismissing French dressing as being far too easy.

'It's very important to do it properly,' Aunt Fleur said in an offended voice.

'Oh, sure, I can see that,' Max soothed.

Elizabeth met Vicky's eyes and they both laughed. The doorbell went and Max walked out of the kitchen. 'I'll get it,' he said, as though he lived there. They heard him open the front door, there was a murmur, then Max called: 'Liz, honey, someone to see you.'

Elizabeth frowned. 'For me?' She went out and in the small hallway saw Max bluntly inspecting Yves de Lavalle, his brown eyes curious as they ran over the other man.

Elizabeth stopped in her tracks. 'Oh, it's you.'

Max's head swung round to stare at her, alert to her tone.

'I want to talk to you,' said Yves, and Max looked back at him with quick assessment.

'I'm very busy,' Elizabeth said frostily.

Max's head turned her way again. Yves took a step towards her and Max was suddenly between them, large and pugnacious and clearly intending to be hard to shift.

'She's busy,' he underlined for Yves in a throaty growl.

'Get out of my way,' Yves told him tersely.

Max squared his shoulders, feet apart. 'Mister, there's the door—use it. The lady is busy.'

'I am not leaving until I've spoken to her.'
Yves sounded calm, but there was steel beneath
the silky tone.

Elizabeth was afraid that Max would hit him,
he was quite capable of it—Max had grown up in
a very tough area, he wouldn't back off from a
fight, and he was built like a house. If he hit Yves
he might hurt him badly.

'Leave it, Max,' she said, stepping round him
to face Yves. 'I'll talk to him, give us five
minutes.'

Max studied her, scowling. 'Sure?'

'Yes, come in to this room, Monsieur de
Lavalle,' she said, gesturing.

Max held up a hand in front of Yves's face, his
stubby fingers spread wide. 'Five minutes and
I'm coming back,' he said.

Yves gave him a coolly insolent stare, said
nothing, but walked past him as if Max didn't
exist. Max did not like that, he went dark red and
made grumbling noises like a kettle about to boil.
Elizabeth impulsively kissed his cheek, standing
on tiptoe to do it.

'Don't worry, nothing's wrong,' she said, and
followed Yves into the sitting-room. Vicky was
curled up in an armchair with her hands behind
her head, a curious expression on her face,
watching Yves as he stood waiting for Elizabeth.

'Vicky, would you mind ...' Elizabeth
murmured.

'Okay,' said Vicky, reluctantly uncurling herself. She sauntered out and Yves closed the door
behind her. Elizabeth decided to sit down and
chose a chair as far away from Yves as possible.

'I thought you and your wife had gone to
Antibes,' she said coldly.

Yves turned to face her. He was wearing a dark
grey suit and a striped blue shirt with a tie in a
darker shade of blue. His black hair was brushed
smoothly, his face as pale as ever, he looked
elegant and controlled again. It was hard to
believe, looking at him now, that he had ever
dropped that cold mask.

There was a long silence while she waited for
him to say whatever he had come to say.
Elizabeth wasn't sure what she was expecting,
but it certainly wasn't what he actually said.

'She isn't my wife.'

Elizabeth thought she had misheard him for a
moment. 'Isn't . . .' she stammered, staring.

'My wife,' he said flatly. 'Chantal is in Antibes,
by now, I imagine. I last saw her in Paris the day
before yesterday.'

Elizabeth was dazed. What was he talking
about? 'Chantal . . .' she began, and broke off,
swallowing. 'What do you mean—she isn't your
wife?' Had he gone completely out of his mind?
Did he mean he and Chantal had never been
married? But that couldn't be true—Aunt Fleur
had mentioned meeting his parents, surely, and if
Chantal and he had not been married they
couldn't have kept it from the village for long. In
a small community, people talk endlessly about
their neighbours, especially neighbours like
Chantal and Yves.

He gave a strange, harsh sigh. 'Elizabeth,
there's so much to tell you. I don't know where
to begin—it's crazy.'

Was he intending to get a divorce? she
wondered suddenly, frowning. He walked to the
window and then back again, restlessly.

'I phrased that the wrong way around,' he said,
halting to look at her, his dark eyes oddly almost
pleading. 'I should have said—I'm not her
husband.'

Elizabeth sat upright, very tense, her hands
clenching on the arms of the chair. Inside, she
was shaking, her mind leaping towards a huge
question mark, which had no question attached to
it. 'What?' she whispered.

'I am not Yves de Lavalle,' he said huskily.

Every trace of colour left her face. Anger leapt
up inside her, poured through her, like smoke
through the window of a burning room, the
fumes of it clouding her mind so that she couldn't
think properly, couldn't even speak coherently.
She could only stammer in broken phrases,
shaking her head.

'Don't try to ... my God, you don't expect me
to believe ... I won't listen to you!'

He moved abruptly, knelt down by her chair.
She shrank as he put out his hand and he let it
fall by his side, frowning.

'Keep calm, my love,' he said, and she looked
at him bitterly.

'Don't call me that! Don't use that word to
me!'

'You know ...' he began, and she interrupted,
her voice rising.

'I don't know anything except this—you're
trying to drive me out of my mind! What you're
saying ... implying ... half hints, little throw-

away remarks . . . it's all madness. I know what you're trying to do to me and I won't let you. You're not doing that to me, you're not making me as crazy as you are.' She put her hands over her face, her fingers trembling. 'Go away, I'm not listening to you.'

He pulled her hands down, she struggled to get free and was tethered by the powerful fingers. He kept his eyes on her face and said quietly: 'But you knew at once, didn't you? The first night you arrived?'

Her heart stopped, with a great crash, then began again erratically, half deafening her. She felt the beat of it in her throat, in her ears, in her head.

'No,' she whispered, staring into those deep, dark eyes. 'He's dead, he's dead . . . you're not Damian, you're Yves de Lavalle.'

CHAPTER TEN

'You know I'm Damian,' he said in a husky voice, watching her face. 'You knew at once, didn't you? You ran into my arms and said my name—I didn't know who you were, I couldn't see you properly in the dark, but you called me Damian and the shock almost blew my mind.'

'I was distraught, I didn't know what I was doing!'

'You knew,' he said. 'God knows how—woman's intuition, I suppose—I'll never laugh at it again.' There was a glinting amusement in his face for a second, but Elizabeth didn't smile back. He might be getting fun out of what he was doing, but she saw nothing funny in the situation.

'Is Chantal in this?' she asked with a sting in her voice. 'Did the two of you plan it together? That must have been fun!' She hoped the biting tone she used would get home to him how angry she was, and it succeeded.

His face darkened, he caught her shoulders and dragged her, struggling wildly, into his arms. She couldn't bear to have him kiss her again, each time he did she began by hating him and trying to fight him off and ended in burning response which tortured her when she remembered it later. She flung her head backwards, turning it aside, trembling violently as she waited for him to try to kiss her. She could scream, of course—and then Max would come charging in here like an angry bull, and there would be a fight. She didn't want that sort of scene—it would be both embarrassing and frightening. Yves de Lavalle was unpredictable, dangerous, she couldn't guess what he would do next, and she could not bear the idea of Max and Aunt Fleur knowing what had been going on, they would stare and look at her in a way she would hate.

His arm went round her, slid down her back and pressed her towards him, but he didn't try to kiss her. She felt him watching her, it sent tremors of fear and awareness through her body, and then she felt the slow, inexorable rise of desire inside herself, hated it, despised it, but could not halt it while he held her so close. Her throat closed convulsively, she felt her mouth go dry, perspiration broke out on her forehead.

'Who am I?' he whispered then, and her nerves jumped wildly, like a needle jumping a track on a record, a long, whining scratch of sound in her brain.

She wouldn't answer him, she couldn't; she was too absorbed in a struggle with her own emotions. Her mind might keep up a steady tattoo of warning, but her body was no longer listening, it was dissolving in a heated sweetness, she longed to close her eyes and lift her mouth for the touch of his, her hands fluttered out to grasp his shirt as her head swam dizzily. He looked down at her, the dark eyes hypnotic, gleaming like the eyes of an animal in the night, she drowned in them, her own eyes drowsy with

desire and he slowly lowered his head to take the
mouth she helplessly lifted to him.

Limp, boneless, she clung to him, her arms
round his neck now, and their lips merged in
hungry, sensuous exploration. It no longer seemed
to matter who he was or why he was holding her,
she forgot everything but the necessary joy of
being in his arms.

When he lifted his head she was half fainting,
her eyes closed. 'Who am I?' he whispered again,
and her bruised mouth silently framed his name.

'Say it aloud,' he said softly.

'Damian . . .' she breathed, her voice catching,
then her eyes flew open and she went white and
thrust him away, shaking her head violently. 'No!
You tricked me, do you think I don't know what
you're trying to do? You want to drive me mad,
but I won't let you do that to me. You confused
me, I didn't know what I was saying.'

'Sit down,' he said, and pushed her into her
chair. He drew up another chair and sat down on
it, leaning towards her. 'Before I could talk to
you I had to be certain—and stop looking at me
like that, Liz. I'm perfectly sane and so are you. I
didn't realise the truth with a thunderclap—it
dawned on me slowly, it came together like the
scattered pieces of a jigsaw. At first I thought it
was crazy, I told myself I was having some sort of
nervous breakdown, but there's no doubt about
it. I *am* Damian Hayes.'

'No!' she denied with fury. 'Stop saying that!
Don't you think everyone would know if you
were? His face was nothing like yours—look in a
mirror!'

'Do you think I haven't?'

'And you saw Yves de Lavalle's face!'

He looked at her, his mouth level. 'Yes, I saw his face—that was totally disorientating. You've no idea how weird it was to look into a mirror and see another man's face instead of your own.'

She looked at him then differently, with compassion and anxiety for him rather than herself, and saw that his face was drawn and haggard, the light fell on it and showed her lines she had never seen before. His features had always looked so smooth and untouched, a plastic mask without emotion.

'You're ill,' she said quite gently. 'You've been under a terrible strain ever since the accident—all those operations, those months in hospitals, the pain—it's quite understandable, Yves.'

'Not Yves,' he said harshly. 'Damian. I'm Damian.'

'You've been feeling guilty because you survived and he didn't, it's preyed on your mind.' She kept up the low, soft tone, trying to soothe him.

'Look,' he said, and held up his two hands in front of her, their long sinewy fingers spread wide, splayed for her in vulnerable inaction.

Elizabeth looked, bewildered.

'My hands,' he said, and flexed the fingers. '*Mine*—don't you see?' He got up in a jerky movement, looking around. 'Have you got some paper?'

Elizabeth got up, too, startled. 'Paper?' he was acting again in that erratic, unpredictable way, his mind moving off at a tangent.

Vicky had left her writing pad on the table. He saw it, leapt over to pick it up, picked up Vicky's fountain pen, too. Elizabeth watched him, her mouth dry with tension. What now?

He flipped open the pad, looked at her, a quick sideways look, then uncapped the pen and began to sketch; rapidly, fluidly, just looking up once or twice at her. Then he thrust the pad at her and she looked at the few lines on it and saw herself: immediately present on the page, undeniably herself, sketched in one minute.

Elizabeth pushed the book away. 'I already know you can copy his style—it isn't difficult to fake, is it? Any trained artist could do as much.'

'Yves couldn't draw a straight line!' he said fiercely.

'*You're* Yves!' she threw back, her voice rising. 'You're not Damian, you've talked yourself into believing you are, but your face is nothing like his.'

'Not *now*,' he said as though he was reasoning with a fool. 'Don't you see? It's not like it *now*.'

Elizabeth shrank, wondering if she ought to call for help before it was too late. He was talking madness in a voice of pure reason, but wasn't that a sign of a mind out of all touch with reality?

'Why don't we sit down and talk about it quietly,' she said, being careful not to look towards the door. If she could get away she could ask Aunt Fleur to ring the local doctor. He was a sick man. Who had said that? Chantal, of course. Oh, she had known what she was talking about! Had she realised Yves was going mad? No wonder she had looked so disturbed and anxious whenever Elizabeth saw her.

He was staring at her, his mouth impatient. 'You don't believe a word I'm saying, do you?'

'Of course I do,' she said soothingly.

His hands shot out, he made a snarling noise, and Elizabeth gave a panic-stricken cry as he grabbed her arms and shook her.

'Don't pretend to humour me, for God's sake! I'm not crazy! I know what I'm saying—they gave me his face, don't you understand?'

She was trembling so much she couldn't even struggle to get away. He pushed her backwards into her chair and bent to speak with harsh emphasis: 'Sit there and listen to me, Elizabeth, and listen properly.'

She wove her fingers together in her lap to stop them shaking. He mustn't guess how scared she was, she had to convince him she was quite calm, the way you would convince a dangerous animal by staring it in the eyes and hoping it would back down.

'It isn't just what my hands can do,' he said, holding them out to her, and she managed not to flinch as they brushed her throat. Hands could strangle, and he had long, powerful fingers which could choke the life out of her before she could even let out a scream. She refused to think about that, she kept her eyes on him, unblinking, but her face was dead white.

'Don't you realise how important hands are?' he asked, and she stared at him blankly. He made a rough, impatient noise, a little groan. 'For God's sake, Liz, use your brains! Fingerprints!'

Her whole mind jerked with shock. 'Fingerprints?' she whispered as it dawned on her what he meant, and then her heart began to beat so fast she felt sick, her green eyes glowed with sudden, fierce hope and excitement.

He smiled at her, watching the stunned look in her eyes. 'It was so simple once I'd actually started to realise—they'd given me a new face, but they couldn't change my fingerprints.' His eyes held the same excitement she felt. 'Or my blood group! I have a very rare blood group, only a few thousand people in France have it, and Yves wasn't one of them. In all the confusion the night of the crash, they didn't check his Paris medical file, they just did a blood test on the spot and started pumping blood into me. I'd lost gallons of it, I'd have died if I hadn't been given an immediate transfusion. They weren't worrying about identity, just saving my life.'

'But later . . .' she began, afraid to believe him because she wanted to believe too much, he might still be lying to her.

'Who do you think identified me?' he asked flatly, and she drew a long breath.

'Chantal.'

He nodded, his face grim. 'You have to understand how it happened. She thought I *was* Yves, she'd been told it was Damian who had died. She had waved us off from the Château and I'd been driving then—of course, when they told her the driver had been killed she assumed that it was me who was dead, it never entered her head that it could have been Yves driving when we crashed.'

Elizabeth thought of something, her face altering. 'But Aunt Fleur saw you at the wheel when you drove past her house!'

'That's right, I waved to her. We had the top down, it was a warm evening and we'd both had too much wine. I waved to your aunt and a bee stung my hand. I pulled up round the corner immediately. My hand was already swelling—I'm allergic to bee-stings, don't you remember? A bee stung me once before when I was with you and I had to get an injection of antihistamine. Yves said he'd get me to a doctor fast. We changed places, he started the car with his foot down on the accelerator and just as we shot off a fox ran across the road from the woods. Yves slewed to one side and skidded straight into a tree.'

Elizabeth saw his face whiten, his eyes very black. He moved away and stood with his back to her for a moment. 'I don't remember much of it, but it sounded as if all hell had broken loose . . . everything went black a second later. I don't remember a thing of what came next. When I came to again, I'd lost my memory. I didn't know who I was or what had happened. Chantal was there, she told me I was her husband and there was no reason not to believe her.' He turned, making a faintly helpless gesture. 'Why should I doubt her? I didn't honestly remember her, but there was something vaguely familiar about her, I did know I'd seen her before. For months I couldn't even move. I was bandaged from head to foot. She never left me. She sat there, talking quietly about our life together. She told me all about myself—about Yves, that is . . . his childhood, family, the bank, the Château. My mind was a blank tape. She recorded on it memories that didn't belong to me, but she didn't realise I wasn't Yves. You have to realise, I wasn't doing any of the talking. I couldn't do more than whisper, my throat was burnt. All Chantal saw was a pair of eyes—she never saw my face, that was hidden by bandages.'

'But surely . . . her own husband? I mean . . . the eyes are usually the first thing you notice about anyone?'

He hesitated, his mouth wry. 'She swears she didn't know for a long time.'

'But she did guess in the end?' Elizabeth watched him, frowning. Chantal had spent so many months with him, she must have guessed sooner or later. She must have realised long ago that it had been her husband who died.

He nodded, face impassive now. 'She says it only came to her slowly, the way it came to me— odd things that struck her, the way I moved and talked. But it wasn't until I came back here to the Château that she was certain I wasn't Yves.'

'Poor Chantal,' Elizabeth said slowly. 'She must have felt terrible.' Elizabeth had been confused and reluctant to believe what her unconscious was telling her from the minute she saw him, she had thought she was going crazy, that he must be deliberately trying to send her out of her mind. Chantal must have gone through a very similar experience, but she had obviously kept it to herself, she hadn't said anything to him.

Why? Why had she stayed silent all this time? Had she been afraid of losing the Château? What would happen now to Yves's estate? There was going to be a messy legal tangle, presumably, until it was proved that Damian was alive and it was Yves who had died, but surely it would be Chantal as Yves's widow who would inherit the Château?

'Why didn't she tell you the truth?' Elizabeth asked, and he sighed, moving his shoulders in a slow shrug.

'I can't answer that.'

He didn't need to—Elizabeth could work it out. Chantal had spent months talking to him, waiting for him to come out of hospital, longing to pick up her life with him again. He had become necessary to her, obviously; he was a reason to go on living and if she lost him as well as Yves she would have had only the great, empty Château and a lonely life ahead of her. Perhaps by the time she realised he wasn't her husband, she had been in love with him, anyway. A woman who has nursed a man through such a long and difficult illness couldn't help getting deeply involved with him, by the time he came home to the Château she must have transferred her love for Yves to him without even being aware of what she was doing.

She had shown Elizabeth such bitter hostility each time they met, even to the extent of trying to run her down that day in the lane. Chantal had been frightened in case Elizabeth triggered Damion's memory; she had been jealous, too—no wonder she had tried to drive Elizabeth away, told her to go back to England. The whole edifice of lies might have come tumbling down around

Chantal at any moment, she must have been living on the edge of despair.

Elizabeth looked up and was startled to see Yves's face instead of Damian's, she had got so used to thinking of him as Damian now, and that reminded her.

'But your face . . . how . . .'

He put a hand to it, grimacing. 'When we crashed I was horribly injured, I was a mass of scars later. The plastic surgeon worked on photographs which Chantal gave him, don't you see? Yves and I had similar bone structure—if the surgeon noticed anything odd, he didn't say anything, apparently. He just gave me back the face he thought I had had.'

'I never noticed any scars,' she said, staring at his face.

'They're there.' He knelt down by her chair and took one of her hands, lifted it to his cheek. 'The guy who operated on me was a brilliant surgeon. He hid the scars in folds of flesh so that they wouldn't show except at close quarters. He was rather pleased with himself about how well he'd done the job when the bandages came off, he strutted round my bed with a small army of students following at his heels and boasted to them about his beautiful handiwork. You can feel them if you know where to look.' He moved her hand. 'Feel there . . .'

Her fingers gently explored while he watched her, and now she felt the ridging of the scars, hidden along the sides of his cheeks, under his chin. No wonder she had always felt uneasily that his face was a mask: smooth, plastic, oddly lifeless.

'They put me together again like Humpty-Dumpty,' Damian said wryly. 'My nose was broken, my cheekbones smashed—I was a mess. Heaven knows how they managed to make me look human again.'

'I hadn't even noticed,' she said, aware of those dark eyes on her. She looked into them and her breath caught. 'When I heard that you were dead, I couldn't believe it,' she burst out huskily. 'If you'd been dead I was sure I'd have known— even after I came here, I felt you were alive— does that sound stupid?'

'No,' he said, and the dark eyes were full of light. She gazed into them and her heart turned over.

'But when everyone seemed so certain it was true, I kept telling myself I was crazy to go on denying it. I got confused, I didn't know anything any more, every time I saw you I felt so bewildered. You were one man one minute and another man the next. I began to think you were doing it deliberately, trying to drive me out of my mind.'

His mouth twisted. 'I gave you a hard time, didn't I?'

'You were a bastard!' she said, but smiled; it no longer seemed to matter.

'Chantal only told me about you after you showed up here,' said Damian, watching her. 'She hadn't said much about *me* at all until then. I knew someone else was in the car and was killed, but it wasn't until I'd met you, and hadn't remembered you, that she risked telling me—and then, of course, she lied and painted you pretty black.'

'She did a character assassination on me, did she?'

'Some of what she said was true,' Damian said. 'That you'd walked out on me, for instance—that was true, wasn't it?'

She stiffened, afraid he was going to turn savage, and nodded uneasily. 'Damian, I didn't want to go, but your jealousy scared me, you got so violent over nothing.' She remembered the dreams she had had, her eyes haunted. 'I couldn't take any more, I had to get away. I didn't want to hurt you, but I was getting badly hurt myself. But there was never anyone but you.' She looked into the watchful dark eyes, her voice husky. 'I missed you desperately, when I heard you were dead I wanted to die myself—you never had any reason to be jealous, I only loved you.'

'Past tense, Liz?' he asked, his voice unsteady.

'Present and future,' she said, and Damian bent his lips over her hands, kissing the palms with a passion that took her breath away.

'I was a stupid fool and I don't blame you for leaving me, but I couldn't help being jealous. I was so afraid of losing you.' He smiled wryly. 'How ironic that I drove you away myself! I wanted to lock you up and throw away the key. When I lost you I nearly went mad.'

Liz shivered. Was the bitter savagery he had shown her since she got here all due to what Chantal had told him, or had he unconsciously known who he was and wanted to punish her? 'I've been wondering if I was sane myself, lately,' she said with a sigh.

'I was as confused as you were,' he said drily.

'It was only when you screamed at me that I wasn't Damian that the last piece of the jigsaw fell into place. That was when I knew I *was*.'

She laughed unsteadily. 'Typical: You always were contrary.'

He grinned at her, his sombre face relaxing. 'It was because I could see that *you* thought I was Damian, for all your angry protests. Until then I'd been going round in circles, half thinking I was unhinged, half beginning to believe I wasn't Yves. It was shrewd of you to accuse me of feeling guilty about the crash—at times I convinced *myself* that that was why I was having such crazy notions. After you'd yelled at me that I was trying to drive you mad and told me that I wasn't Damian, it all fell into place. I went back to the Château and talked to Chantal.'

'And she admitted it?' Chantal wouldn't have been surprised when he confronted her. Looking back, it was clear that Chantal had guessed from the minute she knew Elizabeth was back in Flamboise that it was on the cards that she would trigger Damian's memory.

Damian nodded, his face impassive, but before he could say anything the door opened and Max burst into the room, glowering.

Elizabeth looked up, startled, her green eyes wide. Max stared at Damian on his knees beside her chair, and his brows jerked together in belligerence.

'What's going on? You said you'd only be five minutes and you've been in here for a good half hour!'

Damian stood up and turned to face him. 'This

conversation is private,' he drawled, each word tipped with ice.

'He's married, isn't he?' Max accused Elizabeth, ignoring Damian. 'Your aunt is very upset, you'd better talk to her. I'll deal with *him*.'

'Who *is* he?' Damian asked Elizabeth, and there was a new note in his voice, one she recognised all too well and heard with a sinking heart.

'Never you mind who I am,' Max gritted. 'I'm the guy who's going to see you to the door, that's all you need to know.'

'Max——' Elizabeth began nervously, wondering how on earth she could explain the situation to him. She didn't get the chance—Damian repeated the name with contemptuous irony.

'Max? Max?' He managed to make it sound ludicrous, and Max flushed a dark and angry red.

'I'm beginning to dislike you, mister. You're going the right way to get a good sock on the jaw!'

'You overestimate yourself, my friend,' said Damian, deliberately waving a red rag at the bull.

Elizabeth shot between them. 'Max, you don't understand, and I can't explain just yet—please, I have to talk to Damian.' She had used the name without thinking and she saw Max's jaw drop.

'What? Did you say . . .' He looked at her in sudden anxiety, frowning. 'Liz, honey, that guy is called Yves de Lavalle, I heard you call him that myself when he arrived.'

She flushed, half laughing, half nervous. 'I know but he isn't, he's Damian Hayes, you see.'

'God in heaven!' Max muttered on an appalled

note. He was pale and looked so worried that she smiled at him and patted his cheek.

'It's all right, Max, I'm not crazy!'

'No, sure, of course you're not,' said Max with the obvious belief that she was completely cuckoo in his eyes.

She laughed unsteadily. 'I know it sounds weird, but I'm quite sane and I do know what I'm saying. He's Damian—it was all a mistake, he isn't dead.'

'Sure, honey, I understand,' said Max, and his voice shook. 'Look, why don't you go and tell your Aunt Fleur all about it? She's in the kitchen with Vicky.'

Elizabeth knew he didn't believe her, but she had to tell Aunt Fleur anyway and that was going to be a long and difficult job. Aunt Fleur was going to be just as incredulous and disturbed at first as Max was, she wasn't going to be easy to convince, either.

'You're not to quarrel with Damian,' she told Max.

'Hell, no,' said Max with hearty insincerity, smiling at her soothingly.

'I'm serious,' she emphasised, and he nodded ferociously.

'I know you are. I won't lay a hand on him.'

Elizabeth glanced at Damian, who was looking wickedly amused, then she shrugged and went out. Just as she closed the door she heard Max break out in a thick voice loaded with aggression: 'Now, you bastard, what the hell have you been feeding her?'

Elizabeth paused anxiously, but Damian's tone

was cool. 'Don't get so excited, you'll break a blood vessel. Suffer from hypertension, do you?'

'You know she's in a bad way over this Hayes guy, you've been trading on that, haven't you? I ought to beat your brains in,' Max said yearningly. 'What a dirty trick, trying to kid her that Hayes isn't dead, that you're Hayes. I can't believe anyone could stoop so low. Poor kid, she must be breaking up inside. I wish I'd got here sooner, I had a feeling something was wrong with her. I should never have let her come to Europe.'

Damian's voice iced over. '*You* shouldn't have let her come? Are you her owner?'

'Don't get clever with *me*,' Max snarled.

Elizabeth stood there, listening, her hand on the door handle, anxiously wondering if she should go back to separate them before they came to blows.

'What gives you the right to decide whether she comes or goes?' Damian asked very quietly.

'She works for me, that's what gives me the right!' Max roared. 'She's the brightest talent I've ever had under contract, and if you've screwed her up with your goddamned tricks I'll put you through a mincing machine, so help me God! I need that girl with her brains unscrambled. You'll stay away from her, you hear me? From now on you'll only get to her over my dead body!'

Damian began to laugh softly, huskily, and Elizabeth relaxed and quietly closed the door. She did not need to think twice about why he had sounded so tight-lipped—Damian's jealousy had always been the stumbling block between them.

It came flaring out of him, white-hot, whenever another man was anywhere near her. He might have a new face, but no plastic surgeon in this world could give him a new nature, but at this moment she didn't care. Whatever his faults, however difficult he might be in the future, nothing would matter so long as he was with her and alive. Having lost him once, she never wanted to lose him again.

She went into the kitchen and Aunt Fleur and Vicky looked at her quickly, with uncertain, worried eyes.

'I've got something to tell you,' said Elizabeth, then she took a deep breath and began to explain. As she talked their faces kept changing, from alarm to anxiety, from disbelief to outright amazement. Aunt Fleur sat down heavily, a hand to her mouth.

'My God,' she said several times, apparently unable to think of any remark more expressive of her feelings.

Vicky had a great deal more to say, and no inhibition whatever about saying it. 'You've got to be kidding,' she said once. 'Liz, be serious— are you asking us to believe . . .'

'Yes,' said Elizabeth. 'Vicky, shut up, will you, and let me finish, then you'll understand.'

'Liz, I understand now,' Vicky said. 'Honestly, I do, I know how you must feel, I know you were crazy about Damian, but this . . .'

'Just listen,' Elizabeth said firmly, and put a hand over her sister's mouth. Vicky's eyes blazed over the top of the hand. Elizabeth talked and Vicky stared, eyes getting bigger and bigger.

Elizabeth took her hand away. Vicky no longer appeared to have anything to say. She just stared, mouth open. For a few moments they were all silent.

'Surely Chantal must have realised,' Aunt Fleur said. 'Her own husband ... surely she must have known? But then I didn't realise, I must admit, it never even entered my head that Yves was Damian. I've seen him several times since he came out of hospital, and I didn't suspect a thing.'

Vicky was gazing at Elizabeth with saucer eyes. 'But you did, didn't you, Liz? And I thought you were going loopy! You knew the minute you set eyes on him the night we arrived.'

'Heavens, yes!' Aunt Fleur breathed, nodding. 'So you did. How amazing!' She shook her head. 'And I never noticed a thing!'

'*You're* not in love with him,' Vicky told her, grinning.

Aunt Fleur smiled, then grew serious. 'I'm sorry for Chantal—what will she do now? Where is she, Elizabeth? Is she at the Château?'

'Damian said she went on to Antibes—she has some friend there, apparently.'

Aunt Fleur's brow cleared. 'Oh, yes, I remember her mentioning it to me once or twice—an old school friend married a lawyer in Antibes, Chantal went to the wedding not long before the accident. Well, at least she'll be with friends. How tragic for her to believe her husband was alive and then realise he was dead. Poor girl!'

Elizabeth was glad she had never mentioned to

anyone that Chantal had once tried to run her down; she hadn't even told Damian that, and she never would. Chantal had regretted it a moment later, Elizabeth didn't doubt her sincerity about that, but the incident underlined how violent Chantal's feelings had been.

'Yes,' Elizabeth said aloud. 'Poor girl, she's lost both of them now.'

Vicky's shrewd, quick glance met her eyes and in her sister's face she read Vicky's understanding of how much Chantal had lost. Vicky saw a great deal more than Elizabeth had admitted.

The door was pushed open and Max stood there, his rugged face dumbfounded. 'Liz, he wants you,' he said, and she knew that Damian had told him the truth and been believed. 'I'm wiped out,' he said to nobody in particular. 'I've never heard anything like it. Somebody ought to make the film!'

Elizabeth laughed, walking past him, and Max caught her arm, bending towards her to murmur confidentially:

'Don't forget, honey, you're under contract, and I mean contract . . . marry the guy if you like, but don't try to walk out on me, will you? You'd break my heart, not to mention my bank manager's heart!'

'I didn't know you had a heart,' Elizabeth mocked, and he grinned.

'Not many people do—but I have, and it's right in here . . .' He touched his jacket and Vicky said: 'Oh.'

Max looked at her enquiringly.

'Your heart's on the other side,' Vicky told him kindly.

'My wallet is right in here, though,' said Max, pulling it out of his inside jacket pocket.

Vicky began to chuckle. 'He's nothing if not honest, is he?'

'I don't think you have quite the right word there,' Elizabeth told her, going out. 'Max is as honest as Shylock—if you sign a contract with him he wants his pound of flesh, even if you're going to bleed to death afterwards.'

'Call me heartless,' Max yelled after her, 'but keep to your contract or I'll be the one who haunts you next time!' She shut the door on him, smiling.

Damian stood at the window, staring out. She stood, leaning on the door, watching him with contented eyes, too happy to need to talk.

'I couldn't live in New York,' he said. 'But how could I go on living here now? Everywhere I looked I'd see memories, I'd always be looking over my shoulder at the past.'

'New England is nice,' said Elizabeth. 'The countryside is beautiful—we could live in the Berkshires and I could commute to New York once or twice a week, I could work at home easily enough. My contract has two years to run, Max would never let me out of it.'

'I know,' Damian said drily. 'He told me—at some length, breathing fire and brimstone with every word.'

'We could try it,' Elizabeth said hopefully. 'If you hated it, we could always come back to Europe, and look for somewhere else.'

He turned and their eyes met and her heart hammered against her breast. Damian held out his arms and she ran into them, as she had the night she saw him on the riverbank, feeling them close around her in possessive need. She lifted her face and he kissed her passionately.

'What does it matter where we live?' he murmured a few moments later. 'So long as we're together.' He laughed huskily, his cheek against her hair. 'You want to live in New England— we'll live in New England. And not just because Max would knock me down and trample on me if I didn't let you finish your contract—but because from now on I'm never going to let you out of my sight.' He lifted his head and looked at her, a dark gleam in his eyes.

'What are you thinking?' Elizabeth asked ruefully. His smile was teasing.

'I want to paint you.'

'What, again?' She laughed. 'You've painted me a dozen times!'

'The way I saw you coming out of the river,' Damian said, considering her with his head to one side. 'Your skin all green and silver and your hair like seaweed . . .'

'Oh, no,' she said. 'You don't . . .'

'The light came over your shoulder,' he went on, apparently deaf. 'It fell here . . .' He touched her breast softly, ran his hand up to her shoulder. 'Your hair was . . .'

'Damian!' Elizabeth protested, but he wasn't listening. He had stepped back and was staring at her.

'Come on,' he said, and she gazed blankly.

'Come on where?'

'Down to the river—I want to do some preliminary sketches.'

'Not now, Damian!'

'The light won't be right, of course, but we can remedy that later on tonight,' he said, taking her hand and pulling her out of the room.

'You're joking!' she complained, but he was deep in thought and didn't answer for a moment.

'It will be a warm night,' he said. 'That's good—I want to catch the way the water rippled around your thighs, it looked terrific.'

'I'm not standing up to my waist in water all night while you draw me,' she protested.

'Not up to your waist,' he said absently. 'Thigh-deep, I think.'

They were in the hall and Aunt Fleur looked out at them from the kitchen, a smile ready, then asked in surprise: 'Are you going out?'

Damian looked at her as if he had no idea who she was, then said: 'Oh, hello, we won't be long,' and dragged Elizabeth after him by the wrist. She looked back as they left the house and waved to the baffled little trio standing in the kitchen doorway, then she was tugged away as Damian strode off without looking round.

'Damian, wait,' she said breathlessly. 'You haven't got a sketchpad with you.'

'I'll get one from the tower.'

'You're not seriously expecting me to strip off and swim in broad daylight!' She didn't know whether to laugh or hit him. 'Someone might be down there—fishing or walking along the bank!'

'If there's anyone there we'll go back to the tower,' he said.

'You must be eager to get back to work!' Elizabeth muttered, and Damian halted and looked down at her, his eyes full of wicked laughter.

'Work is not what I'm eager to get to,' he said drily. 'Sometimes, my love, you're very slow on the uptake.'

Elizabeth stared at him, then his words sank in and her lips parted on a stifled gasp of understanding.

'I'm glad to see we're communicating at last,' Damian said with amusement. 'I badly want to get you into bed, but there were too many people at that house. The tower is a fine and private place, remember.'

Her eyes glowed, she smiled. 'Why didn't you say so before? We'll get there quicker if we run.'

And they ran all the way.

The romantic gift for Christmas

First time in paperbac
four superb romance
by favourite authors,
an attractive special
gift pack. A superb
present to give. And t
receive.

United Kingdom £3.8
Publication 14th October 19:

Darkness of the Heart
Charlotte Lamb

Trust in Summer Madness
Carole Mortimer

Virtuous Lac
Madeleine K

Man-Hater
Penny Jorda

Look for this gift pack where you buy Mills & Boon romanc

Mills & Boon.
The rose of romanc

ROMANCE

Next month's romances from Mills & Boon

Each month, you can choose from a world of variety in romance with Mills & Boon. These are the new titles to look out for next month.

CHAINS OF REGRET Margaret Pargeter
BELOVED STRANGER Elizabeth Oldfield
SUBTLE REVENGE Carole Mortimer
MARRIAGE UNDER FIRE Daphne Clair
A BAD ENEMY Sara Craven
SAVAGE ATONEMENT Penny Jordan
A SECRET INTIMACY Charlotte Lamb
GENTLE PERSUASION Claudia Jameson
THE FACE OF THE STRANGER Angela Carson
THE TYZAK INHERITANCE Nicola West
TETHERED LIBERTY Jessica Steele
NO OTHER CHANCE Avery Thorne

Buy them from your usual paperback stockist, or write to: Mills & Boon Reader Service, P.O. Box 236, Thornton Rd, Croydon, Surrey CR9 3RU, England. Readers in South Africa-write to: Mills & Boon Reader Service of Southern Africa, Private Bag X3010, Randburg, 2125.

Mills & Boon

the rose of romance

SIX MAGNIFICENT SOLITAIRE DIAMOND RINGS FRO
JAMES WALKER MUST BE WON **EACH WORTH £1,0**
IN THE **MILLS & BOON**

Romantic Partner
COMPETITIO

Simply study the nine famous names from literary romances listed A to I below and match them (by placing letter in the appropriate box) to their respective partners. Then in not more than 12 words complete the tie breaker in an apt and original manner, fill in your name and address, together with the store where you purchased this book and send it to:

Larger
actual

Mills & Boon Romantic Partners Competition
6 Sampson Street, London E1 9NA.

The six winners will each receive a magnificent solitaire diamond ring, worth* £1
(retail value) specially selected from the wide range available at James Walker the
jewellers.
*Correct at time of going to print as valued by James Walker, Jewellers.

RULES

1. The competition is open to residents of the UK and Eire only, aged 16 years and over, other than employees of Mills & Boon Limited, their agencies or anyone associated with the administration of the competition.
2. There will be six prizes of solitaire diamond rings each at

an estimated retail value of £1,000 (one thousand pounds).
3. Competition closes on 21st Dec. 198:
winners will be notified by 16th Jan. 1984
4. For results send an S.A.E. to the compe
address above.

WORTH £1,000
(retail value)

ENTRY FORM:—

1. Dr Zhivago	&	
2. Maria	&	
3. Rochester	&	
4. Heathcliff	&	
5. Antony	&	
6. Nelson	&	

A. Juliet
B. Lara
C. Josephine
D. Rhett Butler
E. Emma Hamilton
F. Baron Von Trapp

G. Cleopatra
H. Cathy
I. Jane Eyre

Tie Breaker:— Mills & Boon is the very best in romantic fiction becau
(complete this sentence in not more than 12 words):

....

....

NAME (BLOCK CAPITALS PLEASE) ....

ADDRESS ....

....

BOOK PURCHASED AT ....